From Womb To Tomb

To Pauline
With every good wish
Ann Robertson

ANN ROBERTSON

ISBN 978-0-9564537-8-5

Cover design: Alison Tumer

Typeset in Times New Roman 11pt

Printed by Berforts, Hastings, East Sussex

YouByYou Books,
Swallow Court,
High Halden Road,
Biddenden,
Kent TN27 8BD.

www.youbyyou.co.uk

Contents

14486

NATIONAL HEALTH SERVICE

This is to certify that

Ann Edith Clayden

has undertaken a course of training in

DISTRICT NURSING

at a centre approved by the Secretary of State
for Social Services and has passed the examination

J.D. Robson

*Chairman of the Panel of Assessors
on District Nurse Training*

Phyllis Friend

*Chief Nursing Officer of the
Department of Health and Social Security*

DEC Bradley

*Nursing Officer of Training
Authority*

Date   10 January 1974

4

Dedicated to all the District Nurses and Midwives
in the Community

The events are true but in some cases the names of people and places
have been changed to protect their privacy.

Chapter One. In At The Deep End

 What on earth had I done? Whatever possessed me to be stupid enough to even consider such a move?

Standing in the car park of a Health Clinic in a seaside town in north-east Kent, on a bitingly cold February day in 1972, I surveyed the ever-growing pile of assorted equipment waiting to be stowed into the boot of my humble Morris Minor. The frisson of excitement I had felt earlier at the prospect of a different job in pastures new was rapidly being replaced by a rising tide of panic.

When the appointment was confirmed there and then at the interview, I thought that the professionalism with which I had acquitted myself must have been quite impressive. The more likely reality was a dearth of other applicants. The post involved nursing in the community and I mentally reviewed my previous experience, which seemed to be seriously lacking in the second component required, unless one counted the six months spent riding a bicycle round the streets of Northampton as a pupil midwife.

Three and a half years general nursing training had been followed by a year in which to gain midwifery certification, and 18 months post-registration experience, culminating in marriage and two children.

Seven years later I returned as a part-time midwife on night duty, in a Midlands city with a growing multicultural population. Here, my main achievements appeared to be the acquisition of a diploma entitling me to practice Family Planning (see over), and that of exhorting women in childbirth to 'push' in Italian and two Indian dialects - a skill which was hardly likely to be required in this rural outpost of south-east England.

Necessity is a hard taskmaster, and a broken marriage with the responsibility of providing for two growing girls, a spaniel dog and three goldfish does tend to sharpen the mind. Paucity in the financial and housing departments forced a return to my roots, where loving, supportive parents provided me with a roof over my head and shared childcare, thereby enabling me to return to full-time employment.

Following three happy and fulfilling years as a Night Sister in a busy hospital maternity department, the assault on my body clock, engendered by constant nocturnal service, began to wreak havoc on my health. This need for a change of direction led me to apply for the vacant post of District Nurse/Midwife at the GP practice in the village next to my home. I knew that the midwifery aspect of the work presented no problems, but it was some 15 years or more since my last brush with general nursing and I could only pray that the necessary knowledge and skills would return as easily as the metaphorical bike ride.

Aware of the slightly uninspiring figure of the Nursing Officer at my side, I hauled myself out of my reverie and bemusedly proceeded to load the pile of paraphernalia into the car, as the items were ticked off the list attached to a clipboard.

"Make sure it's all there, Nurse, because you must sign for this and be prepared to produce the items at any time if required. You are responsible for maintaining everything to a high standard and your performance will be inspected twice a year. Always remember, a clean and tidy car and nursing equipment is indicative of good personal organisation and performance."

I must have missed the bit about the strength and

Suzanne and Debbie with their grandparents

physique of an ox being an asset, I mused, heaving a large, rigid rectangular black container into the boot.

"The nurses' nickname for that box is 'the coffin'," trilled my mentor. "You'll find it invaluable for transporting supplies of extra dressings, lotions, incontinence sheets and pads. In fact, all those things which it is so inconvenient to find that your patient has run out of when you're 20 or more miles from base."

That may well have been its intended purpose, but a quick look inside showed it to contain four uniform dresses, a dozen long, white cotton nursing gowns, a heavy, Harris-tweed overcoat, a gabardine raincoat and a blazer. Perched on the top was a felt hat, which closely resembled those in vogue with some airline stewardesses. "Of course, Nurse, you will now be responsible for the laundering of all items of uniform and an annual allowance of £12 pounds is provided towards the cost of dry-cleaning when required."

Nurse's uniform, 1940-70

"Of course," I muttered weakly.

"Your coat must be removed in each house and, failing a suitable peg on which to hang it, remember that it must be folded like a parcel with the lining innermost, and placed on a piece of newspaper on a convenient chair. You never know what might be picked up in some of the homes you will attend."

It was my proud boast that, so far, I had managed to avoid picking up any little unwanted visitors during the course of my nursing ministrations. Not that they hadn't been in evidence on occasion. But, mercifully, they seemed to show no inclination to share my habitat, which could not be said for some of my unfortunate colleagues. Automatically scratching myself, I reflected that this was a state that I had no intention of changing if humanly possible.

"It goes without saying that meticulous attention to your nursing bag and midwifery delivery case is of paramount importance," she continued, passing me the articles in question. "Inside each of them you will find a card bearing an itemised list of the contents, which must be kept scrupulously clean and ready for use at all times."

Next a large, square, brown box, apparently containing all that was needed for a home confinement, was manhandled into the boot.

"You will find that the expectant mums will usually have taken delivery of one of these a month before the event. However, it's always best to carry a spare in case of an emergency."

"I do hope I won't be confronted with a virgin birth in a stable," I quipped. My remark was received with a decidedly frosty look and I mentally made a note that the good lady probably lacked any sense of humour.

Then came a weighty suitcase holding a gas and air machine, plus a spare cylinder of nitrous oxide, which once empty had to be returned to the hospital for a replacement.

"Will your car be locked in a garage at night or parked outside on the road?" was the next question. Sensing my bewilderment she explained: "If it's in a garage the contents of the boot may remain in situ provided it is always locked. If not, everything must be taken indoors and reloaded in the morning."

It was with grateful fervour that I was able to assure her that my vehicle would enjoy the most superior of facilities in which to park its chassis, whilst meekly agreeing that indeed 'one couldn't be too careful'. The thought of facing the beginning and end of each day with this loading and unloading exercise would have been enough to make me build a garage brick by brick.

"Whilst on the matter of cars, nurse, I think you will find this little chap helpful." So saying, my mentor deftly peeled a yellow sticky disc from its backing paper and attached it to the inside of the windscreen, handing me another for the rear window. Bold black capitals proclaimed the message:

District/Nurse Midwife on duty. Please leave me room to drive away quickly.

"Hopefully it will stop you getting boxed in, although people do seem rather thoughtless and inconsiderate at times, I find."

It crossed my mind that all I needed was a siren and a flashing blue light to stick on the roof to cut an impressive swathe through any stray livestock I may encounter on the country lanes. Giving voice to this thought I was met with another unsmiling gaze.

The whole undertaking was assuming the proportions of

preparations for a polar expedition. However, just when I thought that there wasn't room for another thing, I was handed a very large box file and a somewhat smaller index box with lid. With a gleeful smile my superior informed me that these contained a sample of each of the forms needed to fulfil the requirements of the job. Out came record books in which to detail all home confinements and post-natal visits and a drug register. Telephone and mileage claim forms danced with time sheets, patient records, temperature charts, drug charts and official headed notepaper.

"Good record keeping is of the essence, Nurse, and returns must be sent to central office on the last day of each month."

Trying not to show my distaste or lack of enthusiasm for this aspect of the work I reverently placed them on the back seat. Her final act was to place a solid, hardback diary into my hands.

"This," she said, "will be your bible. Each day you will record the visits you have to make, in the order you intend to make them, and tick them off when completed. That way, should you have the misfortune to suffer an accident or sudden illness your colleagues will know from what point they have to pick up your work. In the back you will list the names and addresses of all current patients."

Thanking her graciously, I firmly shut all the doors and prepared to take my leave, quite overlooking the fact that I hadn't got a clue what I had to do or where I had to go next. I was rapidly apprised of the necessary details.

"Return to your home immediately and change into uniform. At one o'clock sharp present yourself at Roper's Clinic in the Ropewalk, where you will be met by Sister Cooper. She is a very experienced Queen's nursing sister and will initiate you into the role."

With her good wishes ringing somewhat hollowly in my ears I attempted to drive away with an air of seeming nonchalance and confidence. This was somewhat marred by a passing seagull, who liberally sprayed the copious offerings from its stomach across the car windscreen. Had the appropriate facilities presented themselves I would cheerfully have followed suit.

Nevertheless, I duly obeyed orders, and feeling somewhat conspicuous in my new uniform, I navigated my way through the unfamiliar narrow streets of the ancient coastal town, which provided accommodation for the team of Community Nurses covering the surrounding villages and GP surgeries within an extensive rural area.

Despite concentrating my mind on tracing the somewhat sketchy route to my destination, I could not but be aware of the quaintness of the location, with its roots planted deeply in a bygone age. Contemporary buildings jostled for supremacy with dwellings ranging from half-timbered houses of great antiquity and charm to the more solid, grey edifices of the Victorian era and a potpourri of styles in between.

Tantalising alleyways with improbable names disappeared mysteriously into the hinterland beyond the main street, where a busy market was in full swing, and the constricted pavements of the town centre were thronging with a hurly-burly of humanity intent on pursuing the day's business.

In a nearby side street, opposite some old almshouses, stood the Roper's Clinic. Housed in what was obviously a former Free Church Chapel of the 19th century, its name conjured up visions of the town's ancient seafaring tradition as a port. The Ropewalk itself was originally a suitably lengthy, straight, narrow strip of land where long strands of material were once laid in order to be twisted into rope for use on the ships.

I brought the car to a halt behind a small Austin Mini just as the occupant was prizing her somewhat ample form from behind the steering wheel. The figure emerged to reveal a jolly-looking woman of advancing years, attired in the unmistakable uniform of a Queen's Institute District Nurse.

Queen Elizabeth the Queen Mother, reviews
the Queen's Institute of District Nurses, 1 July 1959

12

Greeting me warmly she ushered me into the building and through a spartanly furnished hall. A Health Visitor was weighing a strongly protesting infant, while a volunteer from the Women's Institute recorded the information in the appropriate books and notes, and another dispensed baby milk, vitamin drops and cereal foods from a supply on the table. A row of mothers were attempting to divest wriggling offspring of their clothes ready to take their turn on the scales.

Ascending a staircase at one end of the hall, we reached the next level before making a final assault to the attic regions. Unlocking a door, my companion ushered me into a large store room containing a shambolic array of assorted nursing aids. Zimmer frames waltzed with bed cradles and ripple mattresses rested across the arms of ancient and modern commodes. Large boxes of incontinence sheets, pads and paper towels stood under shelves holding feeding cups, enamel bowls and kidney dishes. It was a dingy, soulless space lacking in both light and air.

"Welcome to Nursing Towers, my dear." Fishing in her pocket she produced a folded envelope. "And here is a key to this select emporium," she said, her eyes twinkling with amusement as my jaw dropped ever nearer the floor.

"I'm afraid you'll soon recognise that we are working in a forgotten outpost of the NHS and such refinements as appropriate offices, furnishings and other minor improvements haven't yet come our way."

"Where do you keep all the records and paperwork?" I ventured to ask.

Seating herself on a commode, she indicated another and suggested I take the weight off of my feet.

"At one time District Nurses and Midwives practiced relatively autonomously from their homes, rather than from group practices as part of a team, and lived within the community they served. Quite often a house would be provided for the District Nurse and one of the rooms was her office where she kept all her equipment and in which she sometimes held clinics. These have mostly disappeared, so wherever we happen to live also doubles as our official base and everything is kept there. Is that going to present a problem for you, do you think?"

Mentally giving profound thanks for the fact that my parents were currently living in a vast Georgian vicarage with disused attics, I assured her that it wasn't. However, I was uncertain what would happen if I ever achieved my aim of finding a home for myself and the children. Space would undoubtedly then be more limited.

The Vicarage

"Well, we must move quickly because there isn't much time to get you acquainted with everything before I start my weekend off," Sister Cooper beamed. "The nurse whose practice you are taking over won't be on duty now until Monday and she'll get you properly inducted then."

Producing some pieces of paper from a large brown envelope she continued, quite unconcerned and clearly unaware of the decidedly sinking feeling which was settling in the pit of my stomach.

"Here is a list of all the doctors in the area with addresses of the surgeries and their telephone numbers, and ditto for your other nursing colleagues. On this list are the names and addresses of the patients requiring visits this weekend, with their diagnoses, the procedure required and the order I suggest you do them in. This one is a list of the maternity cases that could possibly go into labour, although you'll be very unlucky if they all decide to," she chortled gaily. "By the way, they've already been given your home phone number."

Before she could gather breath to continue, I heard myself saying in a remarkably calm and controlled voice: "You mean I'm on my own for the next two days?"

"Don't worry Sister, it's all quite straightforward and routine and, if you really get stuck, you can always phone one of the nurses with a red asterisk beside their name as they are also on duty. It's a skeleton staff because we have to cover for each other so that we can have alternate weekends off. But you'll soon get used to it. This weekend, you'll have what would be your own case load plus mine."

On casting my eyes over the list of addresses my tentative enquiry regarding the availability of a map was met with a huge grin.

"Well, I suppose an ordinance survey will show you where the villages are but won't be much help otherwise. You'll do far better to ask at each house you go to, how to get to the next. The patients will be only too ready to help you."

All very fine during the day, I thought, but not much use in the middle of the night.

I squeezed my rather lanky form into the Mini beside Sister Cooper and we embarked upon a whistle-stop tour of the area, with her pointing out the various surgeries and the nearest chemist. Stopping on the way to be introduced to a couple of GPs, I was also able to obtain the necessary prescriptions that would allow me to stock my midwifery bag with the requisite drugs which, I was gaily told, meant I was now in business.

"All the regular patients have a box which contains the dressings, bandages and lotions needed to carry out their treatments, plus an official envelope containing the record of the treatments and any new instructions. Sign this at the end of each visit. It is also up to you to ensure that the supplies don't run out. Those receiving injections keep their own drugs and a supply of syringes, needles and swabs which we top up. For 'one off' visits, to remove sutures for example, everything you need is in your nursing case. Not to mention, of course, the funnel and tubing for administering the inevitable enemas that seem to come our way," she grinned.

By this time my mind was in a positive whirl and it rapidly became clear that this job was not going to be a sinecure.

"What happens to the morning visits if I'm up all night with a home confinement?" I asked tentatively.

Smiling apologetically my mentor informed me that I would just have to get on with them as best as possible.

"You can always try phoning a colleague before 8a.m. to see if they can help out. You'll have to do that anyway if the delivery is still ongoing so that they know you are temporarily out of action, but normally we just soldier on. The patients are never guaranteed a specific time for a visit for this very reason. The exception, of course, are the diabetics requiring pre-breakfast injections of insulin and any on regular pain relief such as morphine. You will certainly have to ensure those."

So much for re-establishing the natural rhythm of my body clock, I thought.

Turning my attention to what my companion was saying I managed to catch the words, 'evening visits'.

"You won't have to worry about those this weekend as the others have agreed to take yours until you've found your feet."

"What patients require evening calls?" I asked naively.

"Recent stroke victims, the chronic bed-bound, those with incontinence, any requiring injections for pain-relief and the dying - they all need settling for the night," she replied matter-of-factly, as though speaking of shutting up the hen house. I later learned that keeping chickens was one of her hobbies.

Returning to the clinic I bade a reluctant farewell to this remarkable woman. She taught me far more about District Nursing than I ever learned from training courses, study days or books, and I had nothing but the deepest respect for both her and her Queen's Institute colleagues.

Sitting in the car I pondered my next move. It was already dark and the last shoppers and workers were beating a retreat to their homes. Much as I wanted to join them I felt it would be more prudent to at least discover the precise locations of those women whose babies were expected imminently, rather than flounder round aimlessly during the night. Fortunately there were only three but they proved to be as far apart as was possible.

As I slithered along mud-spattered lanes, squinting at signposts, mentally noting useful landmarks and trying to keep my bearings, I could be forgiven for wondering whatever had possessed me to consider such a move.

I wasn't a nurse, I decided - more like a village idiot!

It was with amazement but profound relief that I survived the first weekend without mishap. My general nursing skills and techniques were a bit hit-and-miss and rusty to say the least, but the patients had been extremely tolerant and understanding. Nevertheless, I was grateful when Monday morning came and I met up at last with the nurse whose practice I was taking over.

Sister Bowler was another Queen's Nurse who had served the area well for more years than many could recall and was known and loved by all. She had brought several of the locals into the world and had now embarked upon the next generation. Already past the official retirement age her short, stocky body was slightly bent and showing its age. By her own admission her joints were aching, her sight deteriorating and her memory not what it once had been. Getting in and out of her little Austin Mini clearly exercised her lack of flexibility and her breathlessness was palpably obvious at times.

"To be honest, sister, I can't wait for Friday to come," she said. "I've loved every minute of my time here, as I'm sure you will, but I'm more than ready to hang up my nursing bag now."

"And I hope you will enjoy a long, happy and well-earned retirement," I replied with every sincerity. At that moment neither of us knew that such a reward would not be hers, for within two years she had died. Now, I was faced with donning her mantle, and acknowledged that I had much to learn.

Until very recently District Nurses had worked a geographical patch which could once be covered on foot or by bike. However, the GPs were not restricted in the area from which they drew their patients, nor were patients prohibited from seeking the services of a doctor several miles distant, provided he was agreeable.

This meant that the patients seen by one nurse within a relatively confined location could be served by a multiplicity of different practitioners. Good liaison between medical and nursing staff was becoming increasingly important in view of the advances being made in treatments and health care generally. Thus the decision was taken to attach a District Nurse to each GP practice who would be responsible for those patients only. Obviously this greatly increased the mileage covered and although most nurses were using cars, they were now essential. It also meant that it was not uncommon to see two or more different nurses attending patients in the same vicinity on the same day, which wasn't exactly time or labour efficient.

The practice I was about to inherit turned out to be one of the most popular and consequently the patients were far-flung, being situated in one small town, 16 major villages and the halts, hamlets and isolated dwellings in-between. The surgery building itself was modern in comparison to many, which often operated out of a doctor's house. It catered for 6,000 patients, was staffed by a team of three doctors, one full-time and two part-time receptionists, and was sufficiently close to a chemist shop to preclude the need to provide a pharmacy service.

Dr. Standish, the senior partner, was himself nearing retirement. Short, assured and decisive and not given to sentiment, his rather brusque, matter-of-fact demeanour hardly indicated a good bedside manner. However, he proved to be a well loved and respected, archetypal country doctor who knew all the patients and much of their family histories. He could detect malingerers and time wasters with unerring discernment and soon gave them short shrift, but to those in genuine need he proved a true and understanding friend.

Dr. Chase was his younger counterpart but much gentler, with a wonderful speaking voice, calm and reassuring, and a superb way of handling everyone from staff to patients. He genuinely loved people, rogue and saint alike, and they in turn adored him. He was always there for them, night and day, and he gave endlessly of himself in their interests.

Dr. Rivers was very much the junior partner, whose arrival coincided with mine, and I was delighted to renew an old acquaintance. He had been the paediatric houseman at the hospital and our paths crossed on many occasions. Regarded as something of a workaholic, it was not unusual to find him doing a round of the babies on the maternity unit after midnight. This wasn't always welcomed by the staff who, having settled their charges peacefully in their cribs, were faced with pacifying them after the doctor's very thorough examinations which involved divesting them of nappies in order to test for possible 'clicking hips'. The trouble was that he never replaced the nappies, leaving a highly indignant infant kicking its legs wildly in the air and loudly proclaiming its displeasure! His notes were meticulous and he was, without doubt, one of the most conscientious men I had ever come across.

This then was to be my working home for I knew not how long. The atmosphere was pleasant and the staff welcoming, warm and friendly, so the omens seemed set fair.

The morning flew by on wings as I tried to retain the details of the patients and the wealth of information, instructions and general geography. Lunchtime came and I found myself once more ascending the stairs to 'Nursing Towers'. Perched on whatever was available were the nurses who were to become my colleagues, support and, in some cases, friends.

There were three of us with the dual post of Nurse/Midwife: four general nurses and one midwife. At that time we were employed and salaried by the local authority and between us we serviced seven surgeries: 12 doctors covering some 30 villages, seven hamlets and one small town. In turn, we were overseen by two senior nursing officers, 40 miles remote, who had responsibility for the whole county, and a nursing officer based 20 miles away who met with us once a month or in an emergency. The nearest hospitals were similarly distant.

I was duly introduced and speedily entered names and telephone numbers into my working diary whilst they observed 'the new girl on the block' with covert curiosity.

There was no apparent hierarchy for all were considered equals, although deference was undoubtedly shown to the two Queen's Nurses.

One of the hardest things to come to terms with was the extremely basic dressings. Coming from a hospital environment where pre-prepared dressing packs for every possible contingency were provided by a Central Sterile Supplies Department, arrangements on the district were primitive to say the least.

Where patients required regular dressings for conditions such as leg ulcers, they were given a prescription for a roll of gauze, a roll of gamgee and a roll of cotton wool. From these the more capable were taught to roll cotton wool balls, cut the gauze into uniform squares and the gamgee into pads. These were divided into the required amounts to be wrapped in a paper nursing towel. The finished products were then placed in a tin and baked in the oven, to be sterilized - usually after the Sunday roast. Any instruments and gallipots required were boiled in a saucepan. Despite this seemingly archaic procedure, cases of infection on the district were rare. However, many relied upon the nurse to supply the dressings for them. As a result my two young daughters became dab hands at this pastime and the three of us would sit round the kitchen table preparing the packs whilst sharing our various goings-on.

To my great delight I discovered that one of my induction days was to be spent with Sister Cooper, whose example, knowledge and understanding did so much to set me on the right road. As we whizzed along the lanes and byways, the pearls of wisdom that fell from her lips were stored away for future reference.

General training does not, and cannot, equip a nurse to face the realities and practicalities of life on the district. From being cocooned within the secure environment of a hospital surrounded by colleagues, and where help is always to hand, you suddenly find yourself virtually on your own working in near isolation.

"The chief requirements needed by a District Nurse," my mentor informed me, "are stamina, the ability to assess, adapt and improvise quickly, ingenuity and innovation and, above all, common sense. You will constantly be required to think on your feet and make speedy but safe decisions."

All of which sounded somewhat daunting to the novice.

"There are many plus factors, however. For one thing you are your own boss. There is nobody breathing down your neck and watching your every move. Although the pace can be hectic at times things are, generally speaking, more relaxed. Nevertheless, with that freedom and trust come responsibilities, the greatest being the welfare and safety of the patients in your care."

As we visited patient after patient, the huge social variations became apparent, reflected above all in their housing. It is said that the Englishman's home is his castle and a jealously guarded preserve, although I came to wonder how people could even bear to live in, let alone be protective of some of them.

"Always remember that we are guests in their homes and they have the right to refuse us entry," was Sister Cooper's advice.

While most patients welcomed the District Nurse with gratitude, I was reminded never to take that for granted.

"Sometimes you will have to work hard to build relationships and gain trust."

Mercifully, during my long years in post, that never happened. There may have been a measure of reluctance evidenced on occasion, but this was usually outweighed by their need for help.

"It is no small thing to lose one's independence and part of our role is not simply to go in and take over, but to also help in restoring their freedom and self-determination and to teach them to care for themselves," said my mentor.

"Always try to stand in the patient's shoes," she recommended. "How would you react and what would you want in that situation?" Not yet 40 years of age at the time and reasonably sound in mind and limb, this exercise was pretty hypothetical. Little did I realise how her words would one day return to haunt me when, in later life, I was obliged to subject myself to the ministrations of others for a while.

The patients' homes were of a veritable assortment of styles and in varied states, from immaculate perfection to absolute squalor and near dilapidation. Many presented quite a challenge. Over the years I would find myself in anything from a stately home to council houses, thatched cottages and modern, state-of-the-art residences, ancient manor houses and caravans, even a boat. No matter what the situation, I always found Sister Cooper's words echoing in my ears.

"Although we may turn up our noses, and even be tempted to pinch them on some occasions," she grimaced wryly, "these are their homes, each one to be treated with respect. The shabby cloth-worked rug is someone's Axminster carpet and the cheap 'present from Brighton' is another person's piece of Dresden china. They may seem of little value to us but to them they are treasured possessions."

Here was a nurse who didn't just sympathise with her patients but walked alongside them. Indeed, it was she who taught me that they didn't want my sympathy but my empathy.

"It is easy to feel sorry for someone, to pity them and commiserate," she said. "They are not asking for that. They would prefer instead that you identified with them and showed a measure of understanding. That is empathy."

Some years later when the senior partner in my practice retired, he told a story that showed that he too understood the difference, although with considerably more humour.

There was, he said, a new husband who was so besotted with his wife that he commissioned a portrait from a famous artist.

"I want you to paint her with empathy," he requested. The finished result was stunning, but the husband was rather perplexed by the inclusion of a man standing behind with his hand sneaking down inside the low-cut neckline of the wife's dress. "Excuse me, what is that?" he enquired.

"Well sir, you asked me to paint her with empathy but I didn't know what it meant, so I looked it up in the dictionary. The definition says that empathy is 'a fellow-feeling in the breast'!"

It was these older practitioners from whom I learned so much of value in those early days. Some people may perhaps have considered them slightly old-fashioned, but they had an amazing work ethic, understanding of and ability to work successfully in the community, and were loved and respected for it. The good family GP and District Nurse who really knew their patch, and the families within it, were worth their weight in gold.

I soon came to realise that I wasn't simply expected to be the nurse and midwife but dietician, social worker, physiotherapist, teacher, counsellor and advisor all wrapped in one. This was the appeal and fascination of a role in which no two days were the same. The demands made were varied and frustrating at times and the financial rewards weren't particularly high, but the job satisfaction was probably without equal.

My first day in sole charge passed uneventfully and I reached home feeling quite pleased with myself. Relaxing with a cup of coffee the ringing of the phone interrupted the moment.

"Sister, I'm sorry to disturb you but there's a bit of a problem," said Dr. Chase. "David is a six-year-old boy who was admitted to hospital for an enucleation. Unfortunately he was found to have a tumour of the eye, but the surgeons have been able to remove it intact. He was duly fitted with a glass eye and the parents were taught how to take it out and irrigate the socket, but now bedtime has arrived, they've got cold feet and don't feel confident enough to undertake the procedure. Would you be good enough to pop along and go through it with them?"

"Of course," I responded automatically.

Replacing the receiver, I sank into the chair and frantically cast around in my mind for the solution to, what for me was, a huge dilemma. District Nurses are expected to be superb generalists; the proverbial Jill of all skills and mistress of the lot. However, most will admit that there are some things at which they do not excel. My bête-noir was eyes, to which I had an aversion bordering on a phobia. Simple procedures such as irrigation, or instilling of drops and application of ointment were no trouble but this was a completely different matter. It was a task I had never been called upon to perform and, although I knew the basics, I really didn't feel competent. After much consideration, I made my decision: I would have to swallow my pride and seek help.

Running my finger down the list of nurses and their addresses I selected the one living closest to David. From my brief encounter with my colleagues that one lunchtime I couldn't put a face to the name. I dialled the number which was answered very promptly by the nurse in question. Somewhat apologetically I outlined my quandary.

"I could go in and give it a try, but I am not sure that my efforts will exactly instill renewed confidence in the parents. I wondered whether you could possibly help, or advise me who to turn to?"

There was the briefest of pauses before she said: "Can I ask what made you ring me?"

"Well, to be honest you are the nearest to the patient."

"I only enquired because, as it happens, I was the sister on the ophthalmic ward before I came onto the district. Of course I'll go."

Offering the profoundest of thanks, she merely said: "Don't worry. We can't be good at everything. You never know, you may be able to do something for me one day."

"Anything," I fervently replied.

That incident remained with me throughout my career and was an example I cited to the many students for whom I became responsible. "Never be afraid to admit to your shortcomings for it is a measure of your strength as a person. You will be respected far more for your honesty than if you try to tackle something and make a hash of it."

That lesson in humility proved to be the start of a close friendship which has endured for the rest of my life. Little did I guess then that Mary and her husband would one day be responsible for introducing me to the man I was eventually to marry. Even less could I have foreseen that when that happy day arrived in 1979, Dr. Chase and his wife would host the reception, held in a marquee in their garden, nor that he would chauffeur us from the church.

Call it fate, the hand of God, or what you will, but that uncertain step into the unknown was to mark the beginning of the rest of my life.

Chapter Two. New Life and Women's Health

 For a midwife there is no greater thrill, joy or satisfaction than that of bringing a baby into the world. I never ceased to marvel at the miracle of childbirth, nor did I forget to give thanks when it was safely accomplished. Anyone casually flicking through the pages of a midwifery textbook could be forgiven for wondering how such an act can ever be described as normal and natural in view of the myriad things that can go wrong. Perhaps for this very reason, of the many hundreds of confinements which I have conducted, the only ones to linger long in my memory are those in which the outcome was not what I would have wished for, or those where an event years later brought the memories flooding back.

Ann with some of her confinements

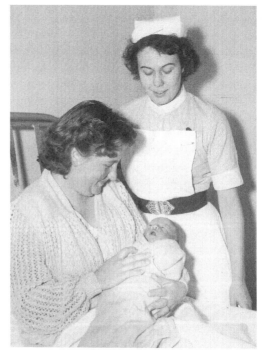

When the IRA blew up the Royal Marine School of Music in Deal in 1989, one of the 11 young bandsmen murdered on that day was 24-year-old Mark Petch. Twelve years previously I had delivered his younger sister. It was a happy event at home surrounded by a warm, loving family. I will never forget the broad smile and look of wonder on Mark's face at his first sight of her. Shortly afterwards, they moved away from the district. I was invited to the christening and that was the last time I saw any of them. Because of its normality, it would have been a confinement that remained consigned to the far recesses of my mind but for that terrible event.

However, before it is possible to even approach a delivery there is something of a hoop to jump through: a seemingly perennial problem for prospective parents is usually deciding on the appropriate time to gather their bags and head for the maternity unit, or exactly when to call the District Midwife. No one wants to hang around for hours in a first stage room listening to others who are further down the line, nor do they want to leave it too late. Worst of all is the prospect of being told that labour isn't properly established, so go home and try again later.

The midwife also has a tricky judgment to make. Whether in hospital or at home, trying to assess the state of a woman's obstetric progress over the telephone is equally problematical. I don't think there are written instructions in any manual on childbirth which state that it is the husband's express duty to undertake the making of such calls, yet invariably it proved to be so. This could be the start of a fascinating, if tedious conversation.

"This is Mr. Y and I think my wife's in labour."

"Right, can you tell me when it started?"

Pause while husband shouts to wife: "How long ago did it start?"

Finally, I glean the information that it is about three hours.

"How frequently are the contractions coming?"

Pause once again while a consultation takes place in the background.

"About every ten minutes."

"I see. Have your wife's waters broken and if so, what time did that happen?"

Further conferral between the couple before the answer is relayed.

"Has she had a 'show'?"

"A what?"

"A show of blood."

So it goes on. I have never understood how the possible onset of labour precludes a woman from actually speaking on the telephone and relaying the information herself. In fairness, though, many households did not even have phones and mobiles didn't yet exist.

Finally a decision has to be made. Every midwife is anxious to avoid a BBA (Born Before Arrival) at all costs. Neither does she want a labour ward full of complete early stagers who may even be there the next day, despite their usually false conviction that the situation can't possibly get any worse.

For the District Midwife the conclusion she comes to can affect not only how much more sleep she might be able to snatch, but the management of the rest of her workload, and that of her colleagues too.

Fortunately, we seem to get it right most of the time. But the results of a wrong judgment would linger and cause one to reappraise the criteria. Thankfully, this never happened to me during my time on the district.

However, I wasn't so lucky on one occasion at the hospital. The phone went shortly after midnight and a somewhat hesitant husband said, half apologetically: "I'm not sure whether my wife's in labour."

"When is she due?"

"Next week."

"Is she having any contractions?" I asked.

"No, just backache," came the reply.

"Is this her first baby?"

"Yes."

"Have her waters broken or has she had a 'show'?"

"No nothing, just backache."

"Well," I explained, "backache is quite common towards the end of a pregnancy and it could well signify that things may be on the move, just not yet," I reassured him. "I suggest a nice warm bath, a hot drink and a couple of Paracetamol, then perhaps you'll both be able to get some sleep. However, if your wife does start to have contractions that you can time, do ring again."

"Thank you, Sister," he said, and hung up.

The night progressed busily and I didn't give the matter another thought until the phone went at 5.30 a.m.

"Hello, it's me again, Mr. Watson. I've got the baby in the bed, what do you want me to do now?"

He sounded very calm, matter-of-fact and cheerful so my

26

immediate reaction was not unreasonable. "You are joking, of course."

"No, if you listen you'll hear him crying." Sure enough I could, and thank heaven for that. The flying squad was promptly dispatched and an hour later a very happy new mum was wheeled in cuddling her baby.

"Why on earth didn't you phone back when you started to have contractions?" I exclaimed.

"That's just it Sister, I never had any. It wasn't a bit like they explained at the classes or in any of the books," she said. "I didn't have anything but backache all the time."

For the next few weeks it would only have required a husband to call saying that his wife had 'big-toe-ache' for me to urge him to bring her in.

A Baby Named Cortina

The ante-natal clinic was held at the surgery every Tuesday afternoon, and on Thursdays I conducted parent-craft and relaxation classes to prepare the new mothers for the event. They were invariably light-hearted, happy occasions and, for many, the friendships forged through a common experience persisted as they supported each other long into the post natal period and beyond.

I usually tried to book the newcomers in first and was somewhat surprised when one of them greeted me with a smile and, in heavily accented words, said:

"I don't expect you remember me Sister? You delivered my little Angelina," indicating a pretty, dark-haired child about four years of age.

Turning to her notes I discovered that her name was Maria Goss and she lived on a smallholding some four miles distant. Strangely, despite the quite distinctive name, nothing jogged my memory.

"My English, it is a little better now, yes?" she asked.

Then the memory came flooding back. Only two weeks before I left the hospital, in the early hours of a January morning, the porter from the main desk had burst into the maternity unit.

"Come quickly, sister. Someone's having a baby in the car park."

Calling to the staff midwife to bring a receiver with scissors, Spencer Wells forceps, mucous extractor and a towel, I ran along the corridor and out into a bitterly cold night. Pulled up in front of the main entrance was a Ford Cortina car. Both the driver's and front passenger doors were open and an extremely agitated husband was trying, without any noticeable effect, to pacify his even more distraught wife in the front seat. Shoving him somewhat unceremoniously out of the way, I leaned in to discover a woman dressed in a heavy astrakhan coat and a headscarf. Her waters had clearly burst liberally over the seat and footwell, and she was shrieking and pushing with desperate ferocity.

All exhortations on my part to persuade her to stop pushing and pant in and out fell on deaf ears. Groping under the coat I detected the hard descending head of the baby straining against the pants and tights the mother was still wearing. Meanwhile, the porter directed the beam of a torch onto the scene as the staff nurse slid in to kneel on the driver's seat.

"For goodness sake, ask the husband what her name is," I requested as I grappled to release the confining underwear.

"Maria," shrieked the now demented husband who was leaping round the car giving a credible impression of an Apache war dance.

"Maria, stop pushing and pant instead. Huff and puff and blow but try not to push."

I might just as well have been talking to a brick wall. Hampered beyond belief by the extreme confines which afforded no room to adequately position the patient's legs, or anything else for that matter, we managed between us to pull down the obstructing underwear. Without further ado, an irate infant emerged to be caught by me and placed on the towel. Speedily the cord was clamped and cut and the staff nurse sped off to place her charge in the welcoming warmth of an incubator which had been wheeled to the entrance hall.

All the while Maria kept up a non-stop stream of groans, wails and incomprehensible babble, seemingly incapable of responding effectively to any commands.

Between us we extracted her from the car and placing her in a wheelchair, hastened to the labour ward to complete the third stage, the expulsion of the afterbirth.

Willing hands divested a traumatised Maria of her soiled clothes and helped her into a hospital gown. I finally received the placenta and breathed a sigh of relief that all had been accomplished with minimal blood loss or damage to the perineum.

The door opened and the nurse from the premature baby unit appeared.

"How's the baby?" I asked.

"Absolutely fine, but can someone give me a name to put on the appropriate wrist and ankle bands?"

I looked expectantly towards Maria and her husband.

"What is it?" he enquired, still clearly in a daze.

At the time, I certainly hadn't paid any attention to the details of sex in the darkness but we were duly informed that it was a girl. This pronouncement didn't seem to register with Maria who simply kept looking at her husband in bewilderment.

"I think I can shed some light on this," said the staff nurse, who had been dispatched to try and find the patient's records. "Apparently Maria is Italian and doesn't speak any English. She has only recently arrived in this country."

Poor, poor girl, what must she have been going through, frightened half out of her wits as I shouted unintelligible instructions to her?

"Will someone just tell me what name to put on this label?" a voice asked plaintively.

"In the absence of anything more definite, you'd better call the baby Cortina for the time being," I said.

Now, four years later, here I was face to face with a small girl who never suspected that she had started out in life named after a motor car. On reflection, I thought that Angelina was probably the better choice as she shyly looked at me with her lovely dark eyes.

"Where are you hoping to have this next baby?" I asked Maria.

"I go to the hospital, Sister, please. There is nobody to help me at home."

"Well, try not to leave it so late this time, because there really isn't enough room in a Cortina to carry out a delivery easily," I grinned.

Maria rolled her eyes expressively before saying: "We've got another car now, Sister."

I forbore from asking what the model was for fear of tempting fate. It might have been a Morris! In the event, she gave birth to another little girl in far more controlled circumstances and I attended them following her discharge home.

It's Not Right

Although I never allowed myself to become complacent, it is almost inevitable that a long run of classic, normal births dulls the mind to some of the less desirable elements of midwifery which can drain the emotions. So it was for me in 1976, which was round about the time that home confinements were becoming frowned upon. Various studies had been undertaken which led to a drive towards 100% hospital deliveries on the grounds of greater neo-natal safety. I was extremely saddened by this, as I loved the relaxed and intimate atmosphere of a home birth.

However, a compromise was achieved with the advent of the domino delivery scheme, whereby a woman could be under the constant care of the District Midwife throughout her pregnancy, and come into hospital only for the birth, which her own midwife would conduct. Six to twelve hours later she and her baby would return home with the post-natal period continuing as usual. It was better than nothing but, for me, it marked the beginning of the end of my love affair with midwifery. Nevertheless, even a hospital confinement cannot protect against some things.

Ruth Swift appeared at the surgery absolutely flabbergasted to discover she was pregnant once again at the age of 43. Today, no one would blink an eye, as more and more women delay pregnancy ever later. However, Ruth already had three children in their very early teens and, as far as she and her husband were concerned, their family was complete. After the initial shock had worn off she entered whole-heartedly into the experience and decided to brush up her skills by attending my parent-craft and relaxation classes.

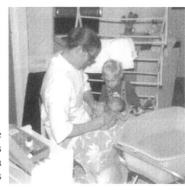

Pupil midwife demonstrates baby bathing at a parent-craft class

Here, she was a wonderful asset to the younger mums and we enjoyed some memorable and amusing moments. There was no doubt that Ruth was looking forward to the new arrival with great excitement.

At that time the presence of the husband at delivery was widely accepted, although still a bit of a novelty and by no means routine. In any event, Brian would have to remain at home with the children, especially if it occurred at night. However, her dearest friend was a staff nurse on the general wards of the hospital and was eager not only to keep her company but to record the moment on camera.

Ruth phoned me in the middle of the evening to say that things were starting. In the privacy of her home we went through the preparation procedure which was then a routine requirement – a pubic shave, an enema and a hot bath. When things were really beginning to speed up I popped her in my car and we drove to the hospital where Cassie, her staff nurse friend, was already waiting.

All domino cases were delivered on an ordinary bed in a single room, without the clutter of extraneous machines and equipment, in order to make it seem as normal and homely as possible. The three of us shut ourselves in and prepared to wait. Ruth's labour progressed apace and by 5.30a.m. we were almost there – it had been absolutely text book. A few good pushes and a little girl popped her head into the world as Cassie's camera clicked non-stop. For both of them all was excitement and happiness, but my heart was leaden. It had taken only one moment for me to realise that this long-awaited baby had Down's Syndrome.

As though on autopilot I cut the cord, wiped the child's face, wrapped her in a towel and placed her in Ruth's arms while surreptitiously watching her expression. Cassie leaned over to savour the moment, only to raise desperate eyes to meet mine in question. Shaking my head at her, I set about delivering the placenta. That completed, I smiled at Ruth telling her that I was just going to clear the trolley and fill in the details of the birth in the register.

"I'll leave you two to get acquainted," I said. "Have you got a name for her?"

"Josie," she replied, almost absent-mindedly, as she gazed at her little daughter.

"I'll come and help you," Cassie offered.

Once in the corridor she grabbed my arm saying urgently, "Please tell me it isn't true."

31

"I think you already know the answer to that," I replied despondently, my mind by now focusing on how to address this difficult situation.

With the tears rolling down her face she said, "Do you think Ruth realises?"

"She is a highly intelligent person, so I'll be very surprised if she isn't already asking herself the question."

"What are you going to do?"

"Nothing for the moment and neither are you. I want her to spend as much time as possible with Josie. Meanwhile, I've got to contact Brian and get him here and I also need to get hold of the paediatrician. For goodness sake wipe your tears away and I'll suggest to Ruth that you help her to wash and freshen herself up."

"Right," she said, the professional nurse in her taking over.

Diving for the phone I hastily rang my father and conveyed the news. The Swift family lived in one of his four parishes and were fairly well known to him.

"Dad, I hate to ask you to do this but I can't possibly tell Brian over the phone. It's a hell of a job. Can you go and break the news in person and ask him to come in?"

"Of course," he said quietly. "Are you all right?"

"No, I'm not – far from it. I'll speak to you later."

Returning to our side room I found Josie asleep in the cot, whilst Ruth was washing and changing with Cassie's assistance.

"I'm just going to take the baby to the nursery to bath and weigh her," I said, "But I'll bring her back for you to dress."

Whilst doing this the paediatrician had arrived and he made a careful and thorough examination.

"I'm afraid you're right," he said. "Do you want me to tell the mother?"

"Not yet," I replied. "I'd appreciate it if you would see both parents together when the husband arrives." To this he agreed.

"Presumably you'll want us to look after the baby until feeding is established?" he queried.

"On the contrary," I protested. "Mrs. Swift has three other children at home and will undoubtedly refuse to stay in. If the baby is left here alone we risk the chance of the mother giving her up into care. It's vital to keep a bond growing between them and provide her with the time and opportunity to accept the situation."

"Down's babies can often be very slow and difficult to feed," he persisted. "Won't that be a bit hard to contend with on the district?"

"We'll manage."

"We will always readmit her if things get difficult," he offered.

Thanking him sincerely, I returned with Josie and laid out the little garments that Ruth had brought with her. As she was dressing her she looked up saying: "Ann, is she alright?"

"Why do you ask?" I said. "What makes you think she isn't?"

Anxiously, Cassie gazed at us both in turn.

"She's just got a look about her," she replied, gently stroking Josie's face, "and she feels a bit floppy. She's not like any of the others."

"No," I said, sitting beside her on the bed. "Josie is different but very special."

"She's got Down's, hasn't she?" Ruth whispered, the tears beginning to course down her face.

"Yes, she has," I started, only to stop as she fumbled for a handkerchief before saying: "Please take her for a minute while I try to think."

Handing Josie to a very moist-eyed Cassie I returned to Ruth.

"I can't take her home," she pleaded clutching my hand. "I can't possibly cope at my age and what about the others? It wouldn't be fair on them. Who's going to look after her when I can't?"

"Ruth, you're trying to go too fast," I counselled. "This is all very new and sudden. Besides which you shouldn't even start to think about anything until Brian gets here."

"Does he know?" she asked.

"Yes, he's on his way now and the paediatrician will see you when he arrives. Just wait and listen to what he's got to say."

"Why did it happen, Ann? Why, why, why? What did I do wrong?"

"It was nothing that you did, Ruth. You know that."

Excusing myself I went into the corridor, just in time to come face -to-face with a desolate-looking Brian.

"Is it true?" he said.

Nodding my head, all I could say was: "I'm so sorry, so very sorry."

"How's Ruth?"

"Feeling much like you emotionally I imagine, as well as being physically exhausted."

"Will this affect her coming home this morning?" he asked.

"No, not at all – she can leave when she wants. Let me take you to her."

I opened the door to her room, ushered him in and Cassie and I crept out as they held each other close and wept.

The paediatrician duly visited, and after much painful soul-searching, a little persuasion and a lot of reassurance, they agreed to take Josie home.

"I'll see how it goes," Ruth said wearily.

So we made our way to their village in a very different mood to when we had set out only 12 hours previously.

The children had departed for school knowing only that they had a little sister. They arrived home desperate to see the new arrival, and were none too pleased when I took them to one side first, having promised Ruth that I would explain the situation. They looked sober and only faintly comprehending until the eldest responded, "She's still a baby isn't she? Let's go and see her."

That evening, I had to attend a ceremony at which my older daughter was to be awarded her Queen's Guide Badge. It was 10 p.m. when I paid my final visit of the day to Ruth by which time Josie's future was all but sealed. The children were fascinated and already quite besotted by their baby sister. Ruth was talking to her and Josie had played her part by taking her feeds reasonably well. They were now a family of six.

Over the next three years I watched with admiration as Ruth poured more than the average mother's love into caring for her precious little girl, proudly proclaiming every belated milestone as they were achieved. It was impossible not to be captivated by Josie and if I was passing on my rounds I would often pop in to witness her progress.

The day before her third birthday was one such occasion, when I found an elated Ruth demonstrating how her smiling child was walking almost unaided.

Two days later Josie was dead.

The sudden bout of croup, which started late on a Friday evening and was characterised by the typical seal-like bark, would not usually be considered a serious childhood ailment, terrifying though the symptoms can be. What none of us knew, however, was that Josie had a congenital heart defect, often the case with Down's Syndrome. In fact, it proved to be miraculous that she had survived for as long as she had. Even without croup, her life span would have been limited but the racking coughing caused by the illness put too much strain on that major vessel.

The entire family was utterly devastated. In the short space of three years this smiling, warm, affectionate child had enchanted them all and made a huge impact on their lives.

On a cold winter's day Cassie and I joined them at the crematorium. As Josie's tiny white coffin was carried inside, feather flakes of snow began to shroud the countryside.

Within a matter of weeks, I accompanied another mother into hospital for a domino delivery. Again, all went well and a lusty little boy arrived. It was only when bathing Peter that I sensed a feeling of foreboding. This little lad seemed to have somewhat foreshortened limbs compared to the size of his head.

Once again my heart sank. Methodically I began to go through the signs for achondroplasia, which is a disorder of bone growth that causes the most common type of dwarfism. One by one I ticked them off: bowed legs, disproportionately sized head, prominent forehead, shortened arms and legs especially upper arm and thigh. As far as I could perceive, this child had them all.

A very dubious, and rather disbelieving, paediatrician reluctantly left his bed to come and check.

"I'm afraid you're right," he finally confirmed. "Well spotted."

This was praise from which I derived absolutely no satisfaction.

Only six weeks later I conducted a home confinement. I breathed a sigh of relief when a perfectly normal little girl made her appearance to join an ecstatic brother and sister.

Over the following days I carried out the usual routine post-natal care with a light heart. One morning, gazing at Mandy lying contentedly in my arms, my eyes became focused on hers, which were wide open. Something didn't seem quite right. The left one appeared somewhat cloudy and the pupil was almost white.

Returning to the surgery I asked one of the doctors to visit in order to have a better look with an ophthalmascope. To my dismay, Mandy was found to have a congenital cataract which ultimately rendered her blind in that eye.

By this time I had convinced myself that I was jinxed. Three abnormalities following so quickly on each other merely served to show that midwifery could be an unpredictable business and there were some things that even the best ante-natal care and a hospital delivery could not prevent.

Over the years, I followed the progress of both youngsters as they grew healthily, and stoically learned to overcome their disabilities. On leaving school Mandy went to university and became a social worker. Peter turned his hand to many different jobs before finally gaining his equity card to work successfully on the stage. Both have married and made a considerable success of their lives.

Sadly Peter's first child died a few weeks after birth but he and his wife went on to adopt a child with achondroplasia. "After all," he said, "who better than us to teach him how to cope with life."

Over the last 25 years, new technology has improved the methods for detection of foetal abnormalities, including Down's Syndrome. The advent of ultrasound can now enable problems of a serious medical nature, such as heart defects and achondroplasia, to be spotted early.

Such technology was unavailable to me or my patients. The midwife in the '70s had only the sensitivity and skill of her hands to rely on. Manual palpation of the abdomen was the sole means of ascertaining the progress of development and the position in which a baby was lying. Similarly, this was the means of detecting whether an infant was presenting head or breech first. X-rays were considered to carry a risk during pregnancy and were only undertaken in an emergency. Consequently, many a midwife has found herself confronted with undiagnosed multiple births.

None of this would happen today where frequent scanning reveals every minute detail. Sonic aids constantly monitor the baby's heart-rate without recourse to the midwife nearly standing on her head, a foetal stethoscope clamped to one ear, frantically trying to chase the elusive sound of the baby's heartbeat across the expanse of the mother's abdomen.

Confidence Restored

When the phone next rang in the middle of the night and a clearly panicky husband implored me to come with all haste to aid his wife in labour, I set out with a certain amount of trepidation.

Arriving at a modest three-bedroom semi, absolutely ablaze with light and the front door wide open, I heaved my gear out of the car boot and struggled inside. I was greeted by the patient's mother and a curious, if somewhat sleepy, five-year-old little boy in his pyjamas. From the front bedroom came the unmistakable sounds of a woman in advanced labour. The spare cylinder of nitrous oxide rattled in the case holding the gas-and-air machine, as I humped it up the stairs with the delivery bag.

An hour later the baby arrived and all seemed well. Bathed, weighed and dressed she nestled peacefully in her grateful mother's arms whilst I cleared up.

"Sister, is this a birth mark?" she asked.

Moving to the bed I saw her indicating a pink discolouration on the forehead above the left eye. Smiling with relief I replied, "No, it's simply a blotch from pressure in the womb. Perhaps a little fist has been tucked up tightly against her face for a while. Over the next few days it will fade and finally disappear completely."

"Oh, that's all right," she sighed. It was a sigh that was nowhere near as relieved as mine. Sure enough, within a short space of time there was no evidence of it.

The little brother appeared on the scene anxious to make his acquaintance with the new arrival. We all smiled as he counted her fingers and toes and then climbed onto the bed to get a better look at her face. Suddenly he cast an accusing look in my direction. "You've hurt my baby," he announced. Pointing to the little pink area he continued: "That's where you bumped her head in that case when you hurried upstairs. Look Dad, what she's gone and done."

He was hastily reassured and I suggested to the amused parents that a lesson on the birds and the bees might be appropriate at some point.

Midwifery had become a joy again.

A Bridge Too Far

Every district midwife spent individual time with her prospective mums and, although there was no such thing as a written birthing plan in those days, the forthcoming event was discussed and their hopes and fears listened to, whilst making sure that they understood the various possible outcomes and were as fully prepared as possible. Whilst instructions were given, most importantly, they knew that we were there to do the very best for them and the baby.

I was none too pleased, therefore, when I received a phone call from the maternity unit early one evening informing me that one of my domino deliveries had just turned up on their doorstep unannounced. Thinking that labour must have progressed apace, leaving the mother no chance to contact me, I was even more bemused when my colleague told me not to hurry as there was plenty of time. I arrived to find Susan sitting with her husband in the room allocated to us.

"Why ever didn't you ring me as we arranged?" I queried.

Before she could reply her husband interrupted, "Because I considered it imperative that we got here without delay."

I had not previously had the pleasure of meeting the gentleman concerned as his work meant that he was frequently away from home. This would be their second child and apparently he hadn't been present at the birth of the first.

"Well, it looks as though your judgment was a little premature. I think you'll find we've got a way to go yet," I commented with a smile.

"I don't see how you can possibly tell as you haven't even examined her."

"Believe me, Mr. Sutton, Susan wouldn't be sitting there so relaxed if things were imminent. Anyway, I shall have a better idea once we've gone through the preparatory procedure, which I would normally have done in the comfort of your home."

"I did try telling you," the previously silent Susan interjected quietly.

"I simply wasn't prepared to take the risk and that's that," he countered.

It transpired that Susan's contractions were only coming every 15 minutes and were not particularly strong. I sensed we were in for a long haul. "I'm sorry Sister," she sighed. "The trouble is that my Steven's fiercely protective of me." Almost as an afterthought she added: "You see, he does like to feel in control of things."

I grinned at her, saying: "He may be in for a bit of a shock then. Mother Nature often has her own ideas."

However, I don't think either of us had any idea how unimpressed Steven was going to be with the concept of masterly non-intervention and allowing things to take their course.

An enema and a hot bath seemed to speed things up somewhat and we finally returned to our room, where Mr. Sutton had been provided with a cup of coffee and a newspaper. We then embarked on an extremely long and trying night during which my patience was pushed to its limits as my every move and non-move was questioned in minute detail.

"I am just going to examine Susan vaginally," I explained at one point.

"Is that really necessary, Sister?"

"I do need to ascertain how far the cervix has dilated before I consider giving her some analgesia."

"For goodness sake, you can see she needs something," he said impatiently, "just give it to her and be done with it."

"What I give her and how much depends on the state of her progress," I replied, my blood pressure rising.

"Don't you think she's been in labour for long enough? Shouldn't you be thinking about a Caesarian?"

So it continued until the first hint of dawn, with every step and action I took being dissected and interrogated *ad nauseam*. Susan laboured valiantly on with very minimal fuss and around about six o'clock I sensed that we were really getting somewhere.

"Would you like to try some gas and air to see if it helps to control your breathing?" I asked. She simply nodded her head gratefully.

"I hope that's not going to knock her out?" said the critical voice at my shoulder.

Once Susan was settled and had got the hang of the mask, I turned my attention to the autocratic, seemingly humourless individual that she had decided to marry. As if by way of conversation I enquired what his work entailed.

"Actually, I'm a civil engineer. I've got rather a big construction project on at the moment so the timing of all this is a bit inconvenient," he explained importantly.

"That's babies for you," I smiled. "They've no sense of timing."

The gas and air machine rattled rhythmically in the background as Susan made efficient use of it.

"Don't you think she's having too much of that?" he asked.

Looking him straight in the eye, I took a deep breath before saying, "Mr. Sutton, you are clearly a very clever man at your job. I wouldn't dream of questioning your ability or try to tell you how to build a bridge. I would, therefore, be equally grateful if you would extend to me the same courtesy and leave me to get on with my job, which is to safely care for Susan and deliver her baby."

Whether my words struck home I don't know, or maybe he was simply tired, but peace reigned at last.

Finally, Susan embarked upon the second stage and, with

commendable control and vigour, speeded the progress of baby Sutton down the birth canal. Gloved and gowned in readiness to receive the head, I glanced at Steven to ask him to put an arm behind his wife's shoulders the better to support her. I was just in time to see a very white face, beads of sweat standing out on his forehead, as his body slid gracefully off the chair to land in a crumpled heap on the floor.

I managed to press the bell push on the wall with my elbow. The door opened and the labour ward sister appeared. Only too aware of the problems I had been experiencing with a certain gentleman she took one look and simply said, "A complete knock-out in your favour I think!"

Susan's comment was even better. "Fat lot of use he's been Sister. He might just as well have stayed at home."

Baby Sutton then emerged as his mother literally laughed him into the world, while Steven was duly revived by the hospital staff.

Preparing to leave for home later that morning, he looked at me ruefully and said: "I shan't forget this night in a hurry, Sister."

"I don't think any of us will," I smiled. "Perhaps you should just stick to the day job and leave the night work to us women."

The Open Road

Hidden away down a track in Willow Woods lived a gypsy family, several of whom were registered with the practice. Although this was their given address, tracking them down wasn't always easy. The entire clan over-wintered in the woods, which meant we always knew where to find them at that time of the year, but come the first hint of spring they would be up and away to pursue their many varied jobs.

The assortment of caravans were dispersed around several different farms where they found employment according to the seasons: pruning in the orchards; potato, fruit, and hop-gathering; cauliflower cutting; brussel sprout picking, and hedging and ditching. Most were taken on regularly each year by the same farmers, who also allowed them to camp on their land.

One morning a sister on the maternity unit phoned me. She sounded apologetic.

"I'm sorry to land you with this," she said, "but we've just discharged a mother and baby to your area and she'll need a visit today."

"What's the problem?" I asked.

"Well, she's a gypsy and the address given is a bit vague, but I'm told you'll know exactly where to find her."

"I presume you're referring to Lola Lee," I hazarded.

"Spot on! She said to tell you that they're out at Marshend at the moment."

"Did everything go alright?" I enquired.

"She and the baby are fine, but I think the night staff on the labour ward went off duty somewhat exhausted. Apparently the entire clan arrived with her and clearly thought they were all going to camp on the unit for the duration. The car park was full of caravans and they created quite a stir as they popped in and out all night to check on progress."

Grinning to myself I reassured my colleague. "They're perfectly harmless but they are an extremely close family, if a rather extensive one."

"Well, I'd sooner you than me," she retorted.

"You need to get out of your cocooned environment and learn to live a bit," I laughed.

I decided to make Lola my last visit of the day. Meandering along the lanes, where fields and orchards were giving up the bounty of harvest, I thought how lucky I was to be able to pursue my career in such a wonderful environment. The late August sun was still beating down strongly as I made my way to Marshend. It might as well have been the end of the world, for it could boast neither church, pub, or shop and there were very few dwellings of any kind save for several agricultural buildings.

In a field adjacent to one of these I sighted a small collection of caravans. The car jolted steadily over the ruts and tussocks towards the spot where a few small children were playing, and an older woman was carefully tending a fire over which was suspended a cauldron of boiling water on a tripod. Recognising Bridie, the family matriarch, I called a greeting as the little ones eyed me curiously.

Bridie was in her sixties and ruled her children with a rod of iron, masked by a deceptively gentle persona. Her face was wizened and weather-beaten which made her look older than her years. Like most of the family she was completely illiterate, which meant that considerable time was needed to explain the instructions on forms and medicine bottles. Recently her health had begun to give cause for concern and she had become a familiar face at the surgery. Otherwise the family usually enjoyed rude fitness and troubled us very little.

"I gather you had a long night," I ventured.

"Honest to God, Sister, I began to think she'd never get there. I'd sooner have had it for her, straight I would."

"Anyway, I hear you've got another lusty grandchild, Bridie. How many is that now?"

"I'm fast losing count luv, I really am. Still, you'll be wanting to see the pair of them. They're over there, nearest the hedge."

I had long since learned that most of the family took considerable pride in their caravans, which were invariably spotless. Lola was lying on the double bunk at the far end nursing her baby whilst her sister Gina kept her company.

"Ain't she just lovely, Sister?" she beamed.

"Indeed she is. Have you decided on a name yet?"

"We're calling her Kizzie," she declared proudly.

"That's certainly a new one on me," I said.

"Don't you like it then?" she asked anxiously.

"I think it's absolutely perfect," I hastened to assure her. "If you can bear to hand her over to Gina, I can begin to check you out."

Post-natal midwifery in the '70s was far more intensive and time-consuming than it is today. It was the custom then for new mothers to remain in bed for three days, nor were they allowed to bath, which meant that the midwife was required to pay particular attention to their vulval toilet, especially if the perineum had needed suturing. This was accomplished by swabbing and douching with water and Dettol as the patient reclined uncomfortably on a bedpan. In this case the receptacle in question was passed round among the Lee clan as and when necessary.

After this the height of the uterine fundus was measured and charted in order to ensure that it subsided back to its normal position by the 10th day. If this didn't occur it may be an indication that some of the products of conception had been retained which could give rise to problems. Bowels and urinary output were checked and temperature and pulse also recorded. The breasts were scrutinised for evidence of soreness, inflammation, engorgement or cracks to the nipple. It was also of paramount importance to ensure that the baby was feeding properly.

After this it was time to switch attention to the baby. Care was taken to see that the umbilical cord stump was clean and that, in due course, it separated neatly. The colour of the stool was noted, as it changed from the initial black meconium through to a more normal hue. The mouth was checked for signs of 'thrush' infection, the eyes for any signs of stickiness and the buttocks for any evidence of soreness or nappy rash. Babies were bathed and weighed by the midwife at birth and on the third and fifth days, after which the bathing was undertaken by the mother.

I was only too aware that these travelling families had their own ways of doing things. Although they would solemnly and respectfully agree to everything the midwives suggested, we all knew that once we had left they simply continued in their own inimitable fashion. And why ever shouldn't they? By and large they were fitter than many in the community, with the possible exception of their teeth which rarely, if ever, received any attention.

Nevertheless, I was rather concerned when, on each visit, I discovered Kizzie lying across the double bed. Admittedly there was no way in which she could roll off but where did she sleep at night? Lola's older daughter Leah slept in a bunk at the other end of the van and there was no evidence of anything remotely resembling a cot.

"She sleeps between me and my man," Lola informed me.

Voicing my concerns that she may be rolled on or inadvertently smothered, she replied, "Don't you be worrying now sister. It hasn't happened to any of our littl'uns and we've all been doing it this way for years. Anyway, it saves getting up in the night if they want the 'titty'."

During my visits seven or eight children of assorted ages would usually be playing outside. It was little Leah who was responsible for the involvement of my two daughters with this family

"Have you got any children, Sister?" Lola asked.

"Yes, and I shall be mightily relieved when this long summer holiday comes to an end and it's time to return to school. Presumably some of them will go too," I said, indicating the tribe laughing and chasing around outside.

"We're not great ones for books and things," she replied. "We move around quite a bit and most of the schools are too far away to get them there easily. Besides which our kids aren't ones for being confined indoors, and the teachers and other children don't really want the likes of us."

The 1944 Education Act had made it compulsory for Travelling Gypsy children to attend school but only for half the year. Despite this many still received no schooling.

"I'd like 'em to have a bit of learning though," Lola said. "I suppose your two wouldn't come and help them?"

For the remainder of my visits Suzanne and Debbie accompanied me and brought with them books, paper, pencils, chalks and the old toy blackboard which they set up in the field. With the children squatting round them they went through the alphabet and read simple stories to them. You could have heard a pin drop and it was a delight to see, although there was no way that anything of real benefit could possibly be achieved.

During my final visit the real reason emerged to explain Lola and Kizzie's unusual sleeping arrangement. As well as ensuring that mother and baby would attend the surgery in six weeks for the final post-natal check, it was also part of our role to broach the subject of future birth control.

"There'll be another one," Lola informed me, "cos my bloke's mad for a son. It won't happen for a couple of years though."

"How are you going to make sure of that?" I ventured curiously.

Grinning at me she said, "Kizzie will sleep in between us until she's two and big enough to move to a bunk. That way he can't get at me! That's what we did with Leah." It was certainly a novel form of contraception which, to my knowledge, didn't appear in any textbook.

Some years after I had given up midwifery I happened to bump into Lola and Gina shopping in the town. Catching up with the family news I learned that Lola had eventually managed to provide her husband with the son he wanted. Apparently Kizzie was streets ahead of the older children, as she had been able to attend various schools from time to time and could now read and write.

"We've never forgotten when you came, Sister, and brought your two girls to give our young 'uns some learning," they said. "If only they'd come more often our kids would have been fine, 'cos they don't really like school but enjoyed those lessons in our own camp. They'd have learned them enough."

I very much doubted that, as neither daughter was drawn to pursue a career in teaching!

Rewards

The year 1975 proved to be a momentous one both professionally and personally. The International Congress of Midwives is held every three years, each time in a different city. The venue on this occasion was to be Lausanne in Switzerland, and to my amazement and delight I was chosen to represent south-east Kent.

Delegates from all over the country assembled at Dover to travel by coach through France, Belgium, Holland and Germany to our destination, where we stayed for an unforgettable week. Lausanne was 'en fête' with international flags and banners across the streets proclaiming 'Le Congrès International des Sages-Femmes'. This was probably the first and only occasion that I would be referred to as a 'wise woman' which is the literal French translation of the word 'midwife'. I can safely say that it is also the only time I have processed the streets behind a brass band! Many of those attending wore their national costumes which provided a colourful element to the proceedings, and banquets were given in our honour.

Lausanne, 1975

This was a unique experience, whose purpose was to share knowledge, network and strengthen midwifery in various regions of the world. It also highlighted the advances that had been made and the challenges still to be faced. By coming into contact with hundreds of midwives across the globe we were able to share excellence in practice, education and research, as well as offer support at a universal level.

The keynote address was entitled: 'A Crisis of Purpose and a Dilemma of Opportunities'. The speaker brought to everyone's attention the risks being imposed by the development of technology and medical skills. This eminent doctor feared fragmentation of care, leading to specialisation rather than total care, which would prove to be the greatest tragedy of our time. He foresaw that the unwillingness of members of the medical and nursing professions to become involved in things beyond their own particular specialty would lead to disturbing results. This merely underlined my own feelings regarding attempts at home to phase out the grade of District Nurse/ Midwife, requiring staff to opt for either one or the other. By the end of the century specialisation would be the norm and the community had lost a tranche of nurses who were not using many of the skills learned and acquired over time.

I returned home wondering once again just how long I would remain a midwife. However, such thoughts rapidly vanished. My parents had brought Suzanne and Debbie to Dover to meet me off the boat. Two excited girls, unable to contain themselves, announced, "Mummy, we've got a house."

The family home

Any attempts to get a foot on the property ladder had been thwarted by the sudden surge in house prices during the early '70s. My modest building society account had grown steadily, but attempts to secure a mortgage were dashed when a sympathetic manager told me that I was considered a bad risk. Apparently I was classed as a young single mother with two dependent relatives, and my ability to keep up the payments could not be guaranteed as I might become pregnant. Opportunity would be a mighty fine thing, I thought!

Thoroughly miffed I went out and purchased the biggest chest freezer I could find. Its delivery caused my bemused father to enquire whether, in the absence of a house, I was intending to live in the freezer instead. Nevertheless, the purchase provided us all with endless hours of pleasure. One of the perks of district nursing in a rural area was the generosity of the patients, who frequently plied us with offerings of fruit and vegetables from their orchards, farms and gardens. This was augmented by days spent at the numerous 'Pick Your Own' outlets, a hugely satisfying experience. Often it was quite hard to keep pace with the sheer volume. But now we were able to blanche and freeze the produce, which kept us going through the winter. This news imparted by the children meant that the freezer would have to be relocated.

It transpired that a modern, three-bedroom detached house, with garage and sizeable garden had become vacant in the village. The property was part of a portfolio of assets which made up a charitable trust. Thanks to the good offices of the churchwarden, who was both a land and estate agent, it was being offered to me at a very modest rent on an indefinite lease. Heaven really had come nearer to earth.

On a Saturday in August the move was accomplished. My good friends, Mary and Fred, hired a removal van and promised extra manpower to help transport the furniture from my previous home, down two flights of stairs at The Vicarage where it had been in storage in the attics, and into our new house. The promised assistant proved to be Fred's cousin by marriage who, although based in Cheshire, worked all over the country. That weekend he happened to be staying in the area. Whilst Rob didn't move in with the furniture exactly, it was the beginning of a relationship which resulted in our marriage four years later.

However, it is a wonder that it didn't founder at the first date. Two weeks after the move Mary rang to suggest that the four of us went out for a meal. In the past any such outing had always depended on whether or not I was 'on call'. Mobile phones were non-existent at that time, which meant that our movements were limited when we were. A few weeks earlier, though, all the midwives' cars had been fitted with radio phones connected to the local ambulance station, whose base designation was 'Gold'. We were each given our own personal call signs which, for some unknown reason, were obscure Irish rivers. I was allotted 'Gold Nore'. Maternity cases and the surgery could now connect with us more easily and we were no longer so restricted.

Having arranged to meet at a pub halfway between our respective homes, I put my uniform in the baby bath on the back seat and set out. On arrival I radioed to Base and gave them the contact telephone number of the venue. Unfortunately, the dining room was fully booked so we just enjoyed a drink before trying elsewhere. This meant taking both cars and my 'date' made the somewhat unwise decision to accompany me in mine.

Settling himself into the passenger seat he watched in amazement as I picked up the hand set.

"Gold Nore to Gold Base," I chortled.

"Receiving you Gold Nore."

"I am now on the road and will contact you with further information."

"Roger Gold Nore, over and out."

Thrusting a telephone directory into Rob's hands I said, "Try to find the number of The Black Sheep – that's where we're going next."

Driving into the car park, my companions waited while I alerted Base to my current location. This exercise was repeated three times before we finally found somewhere to eat. Having satisfied our hunger, eventually we arrived back at my home for a 'night cap'.

"Gold Nore to Gold Base."

"Come in Gold Nore."

"I am available now on my home phone number."

"Roger Gold Nore, I hope you've had an enjoyable pub crawl," said the amused voice. "Sleep tight!"

"Well," said my long-suffering companion, "it's certainly been a novel experience. You've existed for the whole evening on tonic water, so you're certainly not expensive, but I could do without the 'minder' in future!"

So, I thought, there's to be a future.

"In that case I'd better warn you that, under different circumstances, I can be slightly higher maintenance," I retorted cheerfully.

Once indoors Mary found me making coffee in the kitchen.

"If Rob can put up with tonight's shenanigans, he'll survive anything," she laughed.

It was only the first of many occasions when his patience would be tested to the limit. Fortunately for me he proved to have staying power.

Top: Ann, Rob, Suzanne (left) and Debbie (right) after Ann's father
conducted their wedding
Bottom: Dr. Chase chauffeurs Ann and Rob after their wedding

Health Education

Some years before my arrival on the district I had spent a couple of years doing social work with unmarried mothers, many of whom had been placed in the hands of the Churches Moral Welfare Association. At that time there was still considerable stigma attached to such pregnancies. It was not uncommon for a girl to be disowned by the family, especially the fathers, and it was my lot to accompany her to a mother and baby home six weeks before the due date, and help to arrange the inevitable adoption. Since then public opinion and social mores have undergone a sea change, although there are many who feel the pendulum has now swung too far the other way.

Teenage sexual activity has increased steadily and consistently over the past five decades, although teenage pregnancies, having also risen, then declined for a while during the '70s and '80s. This coincided with the increasing popularity of the pill, the availability of contraception free of charge regardless of marital status, and the beginning of a more relaxed approach to abortion. However, with this increase in sexual freedom came the need for more sexual health clinics, as cases of sexually transmitted diseases rose, and the new threat of AIDS reared its head.

This also corresponded with an increased drive for Health Education in schools.

As I had both Family Planning and Health Education Teaching Certificates I suddenly found myself, on occasion, being released from duty, in order to talk to pupils about relationships, sex and sexually transmitted diseases, contraception and pregnancy. Previously this had been the lot of the Biology and RE teachers. But it didn't always have much impact, especially if they were themselves unmarried.

The steady fall in teenage birth rates during this spate of preventive activity suggested

This is to certify that   MRS. ANN ROBERTSON

has successfully completed a course of study in educational theory and practice of health education
at CHRIST CHURCH COLLEGE OF HIGHER EDUCATION, CANTERBURY
during the academic year   1981-82

The course at this college is approved by the Health Education Council

Head of Department

Director of Education and Training
Health Education Council

Date   JULY 1982   HEC(271)82

that young girls are responsive to appropriate intervention and education.

However, such involvement by health professionals was time-consuming and interfered with the daily management of their own caseloads. As a result it was of short duration and by 1990 the trend had reversed. Since then, pregnancies among unmarried teenagers have steadily increased and the UK now has one of the highest birth rates in this section of the population.

By 1980 I had become thoroughly disillusioned with midwifery. There was no longer the same level of satisfaction, as the number of home confinements dwindled and hospital interference, in the shape of medical inductions for no real justification, was increasing.

When given for true medical reasons an induction may be potentially beneficial, but the rationale behind the decision often appeared vague, ranging from the patient being overdue to quite frankly social grounds. Even today, women living in rural areas sometimes have their labour induced for geographical rather than medical reasons. However, it is notoriously difficult to accurately pinpoint the day of birth even with modern ultra-sounds. For eager women impatiently approaching their 'time', medication which is presented as harmless and will 'help' to bring on labour, can sound very seductive.

As with many drugs, there are also risks, and Syntocinon greatly increased the likelihood of further interventions, from the need for pain relief via epidurals, to instrument deliveries and emergency caesarian sections. These factors often created maternal dissatisfaction and were sometimes responsible for post-natal depression. It was so disheartening to spend time with eager young mothers at relaxation classes, only to attend them later, once discharged from hospital, and discover that little of the teaching had been of any use.

As one of them said, "Once the staff had hooked me up to a Syntocinon drip the contractions came with such ferocity and speed that I completely lost any measure of control I might have had. My body had no opportunity to build up slowly to the pain, or to have a break from it. I felt cheated out of what a natural birth should be."

At that time there was no such thing as birthing pools and other recent refinements, and birthing plans as such were unheard of. Far from being a natural process, women in labour felt as if they were merely objects on a production line.

Almost inevitably, there was also a rise in the number of episiotomies being performed. The adverse physical and sexual consequences of this procedure have been known for many years and a good midwife prided herself, not only on her ability to preserve the perineum intact where at all possible, but to institute a programme of good pelvic floor exercises afterwards in order to restore muscle tone.

"Not only will your husband thank me for this," I would grin, as they dutifully squeezed and relaxed the area in question, "you are less likely to experience gynaecological problems later on."

The huge amount of unnecessary medical interference has also proved extremely expensive. A caesarian section costs three times as much as a vaginal birth, which is more than justified in cases of medical need, but not for reasons of patient choice just because someone doesn't fancy the normal route, which has given rise to the phrase 'too posh to push'.

Births are also becoming increasingly complex, due to the growing numbers of obese and older mothers-to-be who often need extra support.

Another change is that women are also leaving hospital earlier, sometimes within hours of delivery, and without the concomitant provision of first class midwifery support at community level, significant deficits arise in post-natal care for new mothers and their babies.

This is especially true in the area of breast feeding, which over the years has flourished or waned according to popular trends. I received my lectures on infant nutrition at the hands of a paediatrician who was absolutely fanatical about the subject. His rationale was positively draconian, as he maintained that there were only ever three contra-indications for a baby not to be breastfed: first in the case of a mother having undergone a bilateral mastectomy; second was death of the mother, and third was death of the baby. If that is so, and if breast really is best and nature's way, I sometimes wondered whether anyone ever informed the baby of this fact. Whilst some took to it as 'to the manor born', there were others who appeared completely disinterested and distinctly uncooperative.

Sometimes a mother's chest attachments proved quite a stumbling block. Thoroughly frustrated infants either struggled to latch onto inverted nipples, or breasts that were virtually non-existent, whilst others floundered, nearly suffocating in a welter of floppy, wobbly mammary tissue. In these cases the skill of the midwife was crucial if despairing new mums were not to be put off. It takes patience, experience and time, which is difficult to provide when discharge home now take place within hours of delivery and post-natal follow-up is fleeting.

Midwifery-led care can result in shorter labours, less medication and fewer interventions, the conclusion being that midwives are the most appropriate and cost-effective caregivers in normal pregnancy and birth. Yet, despite 80-85% of women having uncomplicated pregnancies and births, specialist obstetric care is often still the favoured approach.

Midwives are a unique resource, whose expertise in caring for women and their babies is replicated by no other health professional. Sadly, their numbers have not kept pace with the birth rate in England, which has risen by 22% in the last 20 years, and fewer are familiar with handling the old-style home confinement.

The decision to relinquish my role as a midwife coincided with the increasing number of patients who were being discharged from hospital with terminal conditions, which required considerable skill if they were to be managed appropriately. I had also become interested in the work of the Hospice Movement which was becoming more prominent at that time. I decided that if I couldn't bring babies into the world in the way I wanted, I would assist those at the other end of the spectrum, whose lives were coming to an end.

Well Women

By relinquishing midwifery, I could now put the time previously spent on the ante-natal clinic to another use. Screening tests for cervical cancer had been available for some years and were mostly conducted by the doctors. Women between the ages of 25 and 64 were invited to attend every three years in order to have a smear taken.

Cancer of the cervix was then the second most common malignancy in women, so the decision was made to set up a Well Woman Clinic in the practice, run by an appropriately trained nurse. It included not only the test itself, but also breast examination, a blood pressure and weight check, and urine analysis.

At that time the only doctors in the practice were men and many patients found the examinations intimidating. So the opportunity to be dealt with by a woman at the Well Woman Clinic was welcomed by many, especially the unmarried.

Whilst always maintaining professionalism, I tried to make the occasion as welcoming and light-hearted as possible in order to help patients feel relaxed and at ease. Smear tests are not exactly painful, but nor are they the most comfortable of procedures and, at that time cold, stainless steel vaginal speculii were used as against the kinder plastic variety of the present day. Nor is the required positioning of the patient the most elegant. To the nervous and embarrassed I usually asked if they had read the notice on the door as they came in.

"No sister, I didn't see anything," they'd say anxiously, "what was it?"

"Leave your modesty here and collect it again on the way out," I smiled.

Invariably they would laugh and begin to loosen up.

"What we women have to put up with," was a common remark.

It did no harm to remind them that if men were to be afforded the same opportunity to preserve their physical well-being, they had to submit to some equally unpleasant procedures at times. Most of them hadn't given a thought to the testicular and prostate problems which could occur in their menfolk and it was a chance to urge them to direct their husbands to be checked out by a doctor as well.

When all was completed and they were dressed once more and sitting comfortably, they were invited to ask any questions they might have on matters which may be worrying them. Over the years I learned never to be surprised by some of the things they came up with, all of which were deserving of my respectful attention no matter how trivial, amusing or inconsequential they seemed on occasion.

At that time, magazine articles had become responsible for promoting unbridled sexual activity as the norm, and if someone wasn't enjoying it frequently then they should be. Often this gave rise to feelings of guilt and inadequacy among those who were more moderately inclined.

"What is this orgasm thing they keep going on about?" asked one. "How am I supposed to know whether I've got one or not?"

Women who had previously been quite contented were beginning to question their performance, or that of their husbands.

Similarly, there appeared to be a surprising number in their fifties and over who were only too prepared to relinquish this particular aspect of married life. "Sister, how much longer can I reasonably be expected to put up with intercourse?" questioned one 54-year-old.

I forbore to tell her that two of my patients in their eighties were still enjoying a little romp at times although, 'it takes us a bit longer these days, sister,' they had informed me! This information came out as a result of their indignation at my suggestion that a single bed be erected downstairs to make life easier for the wife, who had made a good recovery from a mild stroke but was finding the stairs an increasing problem.

One woman summed up the feelings of not a few. "Honest to God sister, at one time sex seemed to be the one thing you lived for, but I now find it's the one thing I could do without quite nicely, thank you, if it were left to me!"

Tammy was an attractive lass of 23 due to be married in a few weeks time. She came to me for advice on contraception and, not wanting to take the pill, had opted for a cap which I duly taught her how to use. When she returned for a check-up some three months later, automatically I asked how she was enjoying married life.

"It's lovely Sister – at least, I think it is," she replied somewhat hesitantly.

"Goodness," I said lightly, "you don't sound all that sure. Is there a problem?"

"I don't know," she all but whispered.

Unlike an ever increasing number of girls, Tammy's sexual experience prior to marriage had never progressed beyond strict limits. Clive had been her one real love and the only yardstick against which to measure anything, and TV was far less sexually explicit in those days.

"Try to tell me what's bothering you," I coaxed gently. "I doubt it's nothing I haven't heard before."

"This is so difficult to say Sister, but I'm worried that Clive is, well – a bit queer."

"What on earth makes you think that? I asked calmly. "Is it that you haven't been able to establish intercourse yet?"

"Oh no, that's fine really."

"So in what way is Clive odd?"

Hesitantly she said, "Well, you see, he only wants 'it' on the rug in the lounge."

Not by so much as a flicker of an eyelid did I convey that I found this at all amusing or unusual.

"And you don't like that?" I pursued.

"I'd like it fine enough if I knew it was normal. I thought 'it' was something you only did in bed you see."

"You must have had fun trying to find a rug on honeymoon," I suggested grinning.

"Of course we used the bedroom then," she said, "and very occasionally we do now, but Clive prefers 'it' downstairs in the lounge."

"And that's presenting a problem for you, is it Tammy?"

"Not so long as I know it's alright Sister."

"You know," I said, "we're all different and what suits one person doesn't suit another. For instance, I don't like taking a shower but prefer a bath. That doesn't make me odd, I hope. It's just the same with sex. What some enjoy, others find a bit of a turn-off. There is no such thing as normal or a one-size-fits-all recipe. The important thing is that you are both happy to accept and feel comfortable with whatever you choose."

"Do you know, it is such a relief to know it's OK," she sighed. "I can go home and really enjoy it now."

"If I was you, I'd try to avoid the beach," I teased, "it could get a bit gritty."

Giggling happily she left the surgery, while I gave profound thanks for a husband who preferred the comfort of the marital bed!

However, other problems could be far more complex and distressing. Jill Brownlees presented herself at the clinic for a routine smear check. I had first met her when I attended her mother-in-law who was being cared for in her home during the final stages of a particularly unpleasant cancer. She was as neat and smart as her lovely modern bungalow where she lived with her husband Ralph, a successful London businessman. They had two delightful sons, both away at university, and to the rest of the world they appeared to have it all.

It soon became apparent that the main reason for her visit was not the smear test, but to unburden herself of an overwhelming emotional load.

"It all began once the boys had left home," she explained quietly, clearly finding it difficult.

"Go on," I encouraged gently.

"One day I discovered Ralph wearing my silk nightgown. I asked him what on earth he was doing and he confessed that he wanted to wear women's clothes and often dressed up in my things when I was out."

"And you had no idea?" I queried.

"No," she mumbled.

"There's no need to ask how you feel, Jilly."

"Sister, I feel sick to the core and worried to death."

"I'm going to be honest with you my dear, this is quite beyond my scope," I said. "You really must speak to one of the doctors because you will need expert help and support."

"Oh, I couldn't, I wouldn't know how to begin or what to say," she said, the tears beginning to pour down her face.

"Look, Dr. Chase is here now. Let me go and explain the situation to him for you, then we'll take it from there."

To this she agreed and it proved to be the first step on a long and painful road for Jilly and her family.

There are various reasons why an individual might engage in this behaviour. Some prefer the comfort or style, some like to shock or challenge the social norms, while others want to disguise their physical sex. It doesn't automatically follow that the person concerned is necessarily intent on undergoing gender reassignment therapy. Cross-dressers have complained that society permits women to wear trousers and jeans while condemning men who want to wear clothing sold for women.

However, cross-dressing within marriage inevitably provokes anxiety, guilt, unhappiness and problems if the spouse objects to the behaviour. This was certainly the case for Jilly and Ralph. Before very long the bungalow was on the market and, quickly and quietly, they moved away from the area as he had chosen to pursue the course of gender reassignment.

The role of both district nurse and midwife is a privileged one requiring not only understanding but sensitivity, complete discretion and the ability to be totally non-judgmental or unphased by anything that presents.

Chapter Three.
All Sorts and Conditions of the Human Race

 District Nursing is all about the people who form a positive kaleidoscope of humanity. However, inevitably there is a patient who becomes a firm favourite and one such person was Edith Wall. I met her on my very first induction day with Sister Bowler, little dreaming that she would make an impression on me that would last for the rest of my life.

For nurses in the community, treating patients with leg ulcers was, and still is, all too common. Certainly patients with rheumatoid arthritis are predisposed to developing them. The underlying cause in common cases includes a defective venous blood supply, and the condition can be aggravated by the fragility of the skin due to poor nutrition, trauma or corticosteroid treatment.

Mrs. Wall was 88 years old and lived alone in a pre-war, semi-detached terrace of houses on the outskirts of the town. The décor was dated and faded, but it was clean and tidy, warm and welcoming. When her mobility became increasingly poor, her family brought her bed downstairs into the dining room at the back, so that everything would be on one level. For a while she managed to cater for her modest needs, but now she was heavily dependent on her daughter who lived next-door-but-one.

Vera was as delightful as her mother, whom she clearly thought the world of, as did Edith's three sons who visited her most weeks. However, the brunt of the care fell to Vera who came each morning to help her wash and dress, get her breakfast and make the bed, leaving her with a thermos of coffee for mid-morning. At lunchtime she would appear with a nourishing meal on a tray, a thermos of tea and something cold for supper. Then, last thing at night she helped her to undress and settled her into bed. With the aid of a zimmer frame, Edith was just able to get to the downstairs toilet but she also had a commode by the bed.

Quite apart from her advanced age, Edith had a problem which had been her intermittent companion since the birth of her last child:

stasis dermatitis of both legs, also known as gravitational or congestion eczema, a common cause of which is varicose veins. After a time the skin appears thin, brown and tissue-like and easily becomes weakened, resulting in ulcerated areas. The legs and ankles tend to swell, and painful itching adds to the general misery. However, during the 14 years I nursed this remarkable lady I never once heard her complain.

When Edith's problem first began there was no National Health Service, nor free prescriptions or doctor's visits and consultations. Consequently her children could hardly recall a time when her legs weren't swathed with strips of dressings and bandages made from old sheets, which family, friends and neighbours saved for this purpose. These would be washed, boiled and rewound ready to be used again.

Eventually, aged 76, she presented herself at a doctor's surgery and was referred to my predecessor, becoming the longest-standing patient on her books.

The treatment of leg ulcers was pretty basic at that time and, even when I started on the district, the choice of dressings and bandages was limited. Patients had their own pet methods, often relying on dubious and sometimes dangerous home remedies ranging from Fuller's Earth Powder, Vasoline, Germolene, calamine lotion and herbal cures, all of which were completely ineffective. It was not uncommon for a leg to deteriorate to a stage when amputation was the only option. Fortunately, due to scrupulous attention to cleanliness and hygiene, Mrs. Wall had been spared this. However, the state of both legs fluctuated between fair to absolutely dire and in all my experience I never met another person quite as stoical.

Over the years, as staff came and went, numerous nurses attended her and she was loved, admired and respected by everyone. Sometimes I couldn't help likening her to the 'Little old lady passing by' who Hoagy Carmichael sang about. She had a charming manner, always with a smile on her face, and I came to hold her very dear.

However, it transpired that Edith and I had a particular bond. One day whilst sitting in her living room updating her records, I remarked, "What a coincidence!"

"What's that dear?" she replied.

"Well, I've only just realised that I was born on the same date as you and I have your first name as my second name."

"Fancy that. The only thing is, you weren't born in the same year," she twinkled.

"No, I have to confess that when you come to celebrate your century, I shall be only halfway there."

"Oh, I don't think I shall reach that age and I don't know that I want to. Perhaps I wouldn't mind, though, if I can remain as I am," she pondered.

There was absolutely no reason why she shouldn't, for Mrs. Wall was an intelligent and remarkably disciplined person. Although her whole day was spent sitting in a high-backed chair next to the dining-room table, everything was to hand and organised. Every morning, after breakfast, she read the newspaper and did the crossword. That completed, she set herself the task of writing one letter each day to her growing list of nieces, grandchildren and great-grandchildren, or the very few friends that were remaining. Next it was time to do some work. Edith was very talented at knitting and crochet and her hands were never idle, as she made countless garments for the family. Every new arrival received something which she herself had created to mark the event and Vera had quite a job to keep up with her demands for wool. In time, I too became the recipient of her talents and one day my grandchildren would kick happily on the floor, lying on a multi-coloured blanket made of her knitted squares.

Ann's grandchild playing on Edith's blanket

After lunch she allowed herself to relax by reading and would get through two library books each week. The television was never turned on until the six o'clock news, unless there was a special occasion, and she was always eager to chat about anything that had caught her interest.

"Of course," I said, "you do realise that we share our birthday with someone very famous."

Edith laughed. "You mean the Queen Mother, don't you?"

As I nodded she fixed me with a look before saying, "I bet you haven't met her?"

"No such luck. Have you?"

A faraway look came into her eyes. "I saw her once, many, many years ago."

I waited for her to continue.

"Before I married I was employed as a nursery maid to an important family. One day I had to take the children to attend a birthday party, and who should be there but Queen Elizabeth. Of course, she was only Lady Bowes Lyon then. She was staying as a guest at the house and no one knew then just how famous she would become."

"Did you speak to her?"

"Goodness me, no dear, I knew my place," she replied in her gentle voice.

Over the years, the nursing team tried many different products and treatments for her leg ulcers as they came on the market, and she bore them all with her usual fortitude. Sometimes we thought there were signs of improvement but they never lasted. By the time she was 97 the condition of her legs had deteriorated to such an extent that Dr. Chase agreed to refer her to the consultant dermatologist at the hospital. I had come to know him quite well, as he had seen several of my patients and I always tried to attend the clinic with them.

Dr. Lynton had a wonderful, quiet manner and a reassuring smile. Having observed the state of Mrs. Wall's legs he decided that she required hospital admission. She was very apprehensive about this but was persuaded that it was in her best interests. After several weeks she returned home. Not only were the ulcerations a little better but it was found that she was very anaemic and had also received a blood transfusion. Edith was admitted to hospital on two further occasions for similar care and Dr. Lynton fell under her spell, just as I had.

However, she received a huge emotional blow when Vera had to break the news that one of her three sons had died. We both sat with her while she tried to take it in.

Wearily she said, "Sister, it's the wrong order of things. It should have been me."

The death of a child is a devastating heartbreak for any mother, no matter how old she is.

On 4 August 1984 the milestone event arrived and this remarkable lady reached her century. The family had planned a wonderful celebration of her life in the village hall to which the doctor, hospital consultant and several of the nurses were invited.

Ann with Dr. Lynton at Edith Wall's
100th birthday party

There she sat on a mock throne and, clearly moved and not a little overcome, she held court.

"Happy birthday, Sister," she greeted me. Not once in the years I knew her did she ever omit to send me a card.

"Well, you've made it," I said, "and I hope there will be a few more to come."

"Oh my dear, they've all made such a fuss as you'd never believe. Did you know that a Rolls Royce came to fetch me and I was driven all round the town and the village?" she asked.

"Quite right too, you deserve to be spoilt. And I hope you noticed the Union Jack flying from the church tower and the Guildhall in your honour."

"That's for the Queen Mother."

"Rubbish," I protested, "It's for you and me!"

Taking my hand she held it for a moment before saying, "Do you know Sister, I think there must be something very special about being born on 4 August. Look how long Queen Elizabeth and I have survived, and I think you will too."

That still remains very much to be seen!

Edith celebrated two more birthdays after which she gradually began to deteriorate. The day came when it was considered unsafe for her to be in her house alone and she needed more care than her loyal daughter could provide. It was a heart-wrenching decision, but one which she accepted with her usual grace. She was admitted to a local nursing home where the staff was more than grateful for me to continue the dressings to her legs.

Although she didn't complain about the move, I think we all knew that she now had no wish to live any longer. Shortly before her 103rd birthday, Edith drifted peacefully away surrounded by her family. It had been a tremendous privilege to nurse this wonderful lady and the district felt quite strange without her.

Can Hell Be Worse Than This?

By way of complete contrast, my first brush with the totally indescribable face of life in the community came within the first weeks. Having just about got my bearings and come to grips with my own caseload, I was asked to help out at another practice. The sister was off sick and everyone pitched in to take over some of her work. I received a message from the doctor, via a receptionist, which merely requested general nursing care for an elderly lady with congestive cardiac failure.

The address took me to a tiny, run-down cottage fronting onto the High Street of a small village. The door was at the side of the building and, receiving no reply to my knock, I gently opened it and walked into what turned out to be the kitchen.

It took a moment for my eyes to adjust to the gloom before I gazed aghast at the unbelievable scene. One small window, over the shallow stone sink with a single cold tap, was covered with the greyest net curtain full of holes. To the left was an incredibly ancient gas stove and against the far wall was a wooden table piled with food. A later count revealed a dozen loaves of bread in varying states of mouldiness, nine packets of sausages ditto, and fifteen boxes of cornflakes plus odds and ends of fats, jams and biscuits. The stone-flagged floor was comparatively clear, but curtains of cobwebs hung suspended like some dungeon scene from a film set.

A door to the right was closed and once again I knocked and, receiving no response, entered what was a small living room. The only window looking out onto the street - which clearly hadn't seen the attention of a window cleaner for years - was also covered by a dingy net, and the heavy brown curtains at the side were half drawn. A good fire was burning in the grate and a black kettle rested on the hob. Seated beside it, motionless in a high-backed arm chair, was a figure dressed in an old-fashioned black coat and hat.

Before I could open my mouth to say anything the door opened and a man of indeterminate age appeared. His reaction to my presence was immediate and distressing.

"No, no, go away, go away, not here."

Quickly unbuttoning my coat to reveal my full uniform, I said: "It's alright, I'm the nurse; the doctor has sent me to look after Mrs. Jones."

Squeezing between me and the patient he proceeded to poke the fire in agitation before adding another log.

"Perhaps you can help me," I persisted gently. "Are you Mr. Jones?"

From the kneeling figure came a muffled voice: "Ben. Ben."

"Well, Ben, perhaps you can tell me a bit about Mrs. Jones?"

"Ethel, Ethel," he wailed.

"Alright, tell me about Ethel. I think before we start it would be better if we had a bit more light, don't you? Can you tell me where the light switch is?"

His reaction made me jump. Leaping up he shot towards the door and putting out his hand protectively covered what was presumably the object in question. Eying me accusingly, I was told: "You mustn't touch. Ethel doesn't like."

It was becoming quite clear that Ben, whoever he was, possessed extremely limited intelligence. Furthermore, throughout this brief exchange, Ethel had neither spoken nor made a move. Kneeling on the floor in front of her I gently took her hands in mine and asked. "Can you tell me how you are feeling, Ethel?" The answer was the very faintest of smiles. Reaching for her pulse I was surprised to find it quite strong, if rather irregular. She was beautifully warm, although her skin was dry and like parchment. Slipping a hand inside the coat below the waist, I expected to find her in a state of incontinence yet she was hardly damp. I then spotted the ancient commode to one side of the chair. So my patient must be capable of some movement at least.

Turning once more to the lurking Ben, I asked: "How does Ethel manage the toilet?"

"Ben lifts her," was the response.

"And what happens about food and drink, Ben?"

"Ethel not hungry," he replied. Then, for the first time, I saw him smile as he said, "She likes lots of cups of tea."

"Does she have a bed?"

"Ethel sleep in chair."

"Is there a single bed upstairs that we could bring down here to make her more comfortable, Ben?"

"No bed," was the monosyllabic reply.

Great, I thought. I have a patient who is fairly hydrated but not nourished, unable to move unaided but reasonably continent. I decided not to attempt to probe further regarding her personal toilet, for I daren't even hazard when she had last had a wash, let alone when her hair had received any attention or any of her clothes been removed. It was quite obvious that whatever it was possible to achieve in the way of general nursing care could not initially be accomplished by just one person.

I addressed the ever-hovering Ben: "I am going to get another nurse to try to help me care for Ethel, I will be back as soon as I can."

"No, no, Ben look after," he cried pathetically.

"Ben, you are managing amazingly," I stated with some truth, "but Ethel really isn't well and needs more than you can provide. Don't worry. We'll soon get things sorted out," I said, with rather more hope than conviction.

Once outside, I looked up and down the High Street seeking inspiration which came in the shape of the nameplate on a large house immediately opposite. Walking across the road I knocked on the door of The Vicarage. It was answered by a priest in his fifties, quite casually dressed, smiling and approachable.

"Come in, Sister and tell me what I can do for you."

Furnished with a welcome cup of coffee by his wife, I questioned him about the Jones family.

"I don't know that I can give you much information," he sighed.

"You will have gathered that Ben is very simple or, as we phrase it now, educationally sub-normal."

"Is he her son?" I asked.

"No, he is her youngest brother. From what I have been able to piece together, when Ethel's parents died she and her husband took Ben in and he became the child they never had. There can be no doubt that she loves him with a fierce protectiveness which caused them to become very isolated. They are extremely private people who barely speak except to briefly acknowledge a greeting on occasion. They never have visitors and on my two attempts at a pastoral visit I didn't even get across the threshold."

"For which you can offer up a prayer of thanks," I said with feeling.

"Is it as bad as that?"

"Even worse," I responded.

"What's the present position, Sister?"

"To be quite frank, Ethel is quietly dying. The nurses have been asked to care for her, but there is no way in which that can be managed until we can get her to bed, at the very least. For a start we need a single bed which we can put in the living room."

He replied: "No problem there, Sister. The wife and I have got the one we had for our youngsters still lying unused upstairs. It's seen better days and we keep talking about getting rid of it, but it's one of those things we never seem to get round to. I tell you what, go and fetch Ben to come and give me a hand to help me carry it over."

I managed to persuade a reluctant Ben to come with me into The Vicarage, then left to seek out a colleague to give me some assistance. First, though, I decided to contact the patient's GP.

Dr. Heath proved to be a slightly older version of Dr. Chase. Listening to my tale of woe, he simply smiled gently before saying, "Sister, I realise the situation is far from ideal and I am not asking you to work miracles, any more than I am attempting to perform them myself. Mrs. Jones' body and heart are worn out and she is drifting slowly towards the natural end of her life. I will not hasten that, but neither will I work aggressively to prolong it. It would be totally inappropriate to move her to hospital at this stage, besides which it would be unkind, both to her and to Ben. Dire as her circumstances are, that is the environment she is used to and the one in which she would wish to end her days. Just make her as comfortable as you can. Anything you manage to achieve can only be an improvement. If symptoms develop that require the prescription of further medication, let me know."

Happily, as I was leaving the surgery, I bumped into my nursing colleague, Mary.

"Just the person," I breathed thankfully and outlined the problem.

"Right, let's go now," she agreed. Despite my graphic description even she had to confess that the scene defied anything previously encountered.

True to his word the vicar had set up the single bed downstairs and provided one single sheet attached to which was a note. 'If you need hot water the lady next door will happily provide it. Just knock. Sorry we've only got one spare sheet!'

Of Ben there was no sign.

While Mary collected the water and gave her a wash beside the fire, I decided to explore the bedrooms in search of another sheet and a nightgown. After fighting my way up the narrow staircase, made worse by the piles of newspapers on every tread, I came across two rooms, one of which was clearly Ben's. In the other was an old iron double bedstead. The mattress was devoid of bedding except for a couple of folded blankets, two pillows and various items of clothing including an ancient nightie. A chest of drawers revealed old corsets, stockings, vests and knickers but no bedlinen. The huge double wardrobe had an equally massive drawer at the bottom which I tugged open in eager anticipation, only to be met with a veritable assortment of hats. In despair I looked at the rather grey sheet draped over the door inset with a mirror. 'Oh well,' I thought, 'any port in a storm.' Grabbing hold of it I was frightened out of my wits by Ben's voice coming from the doorway.

"You mustn't touch that. She be most particular about the glass."

"I'm sorry Ben, but we must have a sheet and there don't seem to be any others." If there were, the lugubrious Ben wasn't about to divulge their whereabouts.

"The mirror, mind the mirror," he kept intoning.

"Ben, what's the problem with the mirror?" I asked.

"Lightning, sun," he mumbled.

Well, if the sheet was there to protect against that I'd take a bet against sun in March and we'd just have to risk the lightning.

Bearing my trophies downstairs I found Mary softly talking to Ethel whilst attempting to do her hair, which was in a considerable tangle.

"Have you managed to get anything out of her? " I asked. Mary shook her head.

Between us we set about making up the bed. Vigorously shaking the sheet I managed to catch the edge of a lampshade causing a copious amount of dust and dead insects to descend onto the head of my hapless colleague. Mary had lovely long hair which she wore coiled into a topknot when on duty.

"Thanks a bunch," she muttered, "I wasn't actually intending to wash my hair tonight!"

By the time we'd finished, Ethel was almost unrecognisable and resting blissfully on the pillows, for which I determined to find some cases by the morning and another pair of sheets. She took the proffered cup of tea, which had been put into a feeding cup obtained from 'Nursing Towers' and drank it greedily. With the commode set by the bed, incontinence sheet and pads in situ, and Ben left with instructions to go to The Vicarage if he needed to contact us for help before morning, we departed feeling strangely satisfied.

For five days we visited twice daily and carried out our ministrations under the eye of the ever-wary Ben. The vicar also called a couple of times each day. Later I voiced my concern to him that Ethel could no longer be persuaded to take any tea with her previous enjoyment.

Grinning at me slyly, he said, "Sister, you simply haven't got the knack. I can assure you she's drinking plenty."

Disappearing into the kitchen, he returned with the feeding cup of tea and put it to her lips. With eyes closed Ethel gave a tentative sip then proceeded to wolf the lot with evident gusto. I stared at him flabbergasted.

"She wouldn't take it from me," I said in puzzlement.

"Well, yours didn't have any of this, did it?" So saying he pulled a half bottle of brandy from his pocket.

Looking at Ethel, I said, "You're certainly not stupid are you?" She simply stayed with eyes closed, resting contentedly on the now immaculate pillows.

"I decided a little tot couldn't possibly do her any harm at this stage," he said, "besides which I reckon she deserves it."

I arrived two days later prepared to administer the usual daily care. Collecting hot water from the neighbour, I entered the sitting room and drew back the heavy curtains. Turning to the bed it quickly became apparent that Ethel had died peacefully during the night. Of

Ben there was no sign. Crossing to The Vicarage I relayed the news.

"Praise be for that," he said which reflected my own feelings. "Don't worry about Ben as I've got a pretty shrewd idea where he will be. He's always going off into the fields at the back of the cottage. It's my guess that, simple as he undoubtedly is, he realises what's happened and, like a wounded animal, he's hidden himself away. I'll go after him and bring him back here. The wife and I will take care of him until the funeral."

It was the first of many instances which confirmed for me the importance of the community as a whole working together, and the value of dying with dignity in familiar surroundings, which may be far from congenial but appropriate for the person involved.

There were few mourners at Ethel's funeral. Any remaining family members certainly weren't prepared to take Ben on, and so he went into residential care.

Something Of An Oddball

It was Dr. Standish who instigated another bizarre visit. Charging out of his consulting room one day, at the usual rate of knots, I was peremptorily told that he needed my services.

"Did I hear you say that you were going to the hospital when you finish your calls?"

"Yes," I replied somewhat warily. "I've got to collect a cylinder of nitrous oxide for my gas and air machine."

"So, you could drop something off at the Path Lab, couldn't you?"

Breathing a sigh of relief I willingly agreed. The relief proved to be short-lived.

"Good. Now first you'll have to visit Harry Lane who lives at Rose Cottage in Westmouth. There's a dilapidated, up-turned rowing boat in the front garden so you can't miss it. He's a bit of an 'odd ball', but quite harmless." Clearly this was going to be yet another journey into the unknown.

"He's got mild congestive cardiac disease, but there's something else going on and I'm not sure what. He says he keeps coming over 'swimmy' and he's certainly more breathless. I don't think he's eating properly and he's very pale. He could simply be anaemic of course. Anyhow, I'd like you to take blood for a whole range of tests. We'll do the lot while we're about it – full blood count, haemoglobin, thyroid, blood sugar. And see if you can find out a bit more about his

69

diet and give him some advice. Not that he'll follow it." Thrusting the necessary blood forms into my hand he went on his way.

The hospital van only collected specimens for laboratory testing from the outlying surgeries on Mondays, Wednesdays and Fridays. The taking of blood was not within the remit of a trained general nurse at that time, but was very much a part of the midwife's role and the doctors weren't slow to take advantage of this. It was a procedure at which I felt confident and one that I actually quite enjoyed.

Settling myself into the car I decided to save a bit of time by filling in the details on the numerous bottles in advance. Taking my pen I prepared to print Harry Lane's name and to circle the letter 'M' for male. However, on consulting the accompanying forms, clearly written on each one was the name Harriet Lane and the letter 'F' firmly marked.

Here we go again, I thought.

Westmouth was little more than a street of old cottages. The back gardens on one side ran down to a little creek, largely silted up, which meandered into the river further down. There was no shop or Post Office and only the ancient church, with an old mortuary built to one side of the entrance gate, bore witness to the fact that this had once been a vibrant little community.

Rose Cottage, with its sad rotting boat and overgrown garden, was located without difficulty. Fighting my way through the wandering, choking tendrils of straggly roses, honeysuckle and other unremarkable undergrowth I ploughed a path to the back door, the front one being completely covered in greenery.

I knocked, waited and knocked again. The door opened to reveal the shortish figure of a person clad in baggy navy trousers, an open-neck checked shirt covered by a thick navy blue Guernsey sweater and feet shod in heavy duty fisherman's socks. The pale, lined face was topped by cropped, wiry grey hair. Harriet had made a good job of her preferred gender in an age when such things weren't openly countenanced and 'coming out' was almost unheard of.

The kitchen and adjoining living room were extremely cluttered, but I had seen far worse, and at least it was reasonably clean. I completed my task within a short space of time and turned my attention to finding out a little more about Harry's lifestyle. There was evidence of an unwashed plate and cutlery on the draining board and an empty bottle of beer. Gentle probing elicited the fact that he was off his food.

"I just pick at something when I feel like it, Sister. I used to grow all my own vegetables and I ought to be out there planting things now but I haven't got the energy."

Viewing the jungle of a back garden from the kitchen window I deduced that it had indeed been some time since it had seen any form of horticulture.

"How do you manage with shopping Harry?"

"Well, the neighbours are very good and the milkman comes each day and brings bread as well. Then, I still manage to ride my bike into the next village, if necessary, and that's all I need really."

He paused for a moment before saying: "I've just got to get some energy, Sister, to work on my boat. I need to get it down to the creek you see, but I get so breathless and it's all such an effort."

"Perhaps you could get someone to help you," I said without much conviction. I guessed that the rotting craft hadn't been near any water for many years.

"They wouldn't do it right, you know and, anyway, I've got to keep busy."

Getting to my feet I looked with sadness but sneaking respect at this character. Smiling at him I suggested that we leave any further thoughts of action until we had the results of the blood tests in a few days time. To this he meekly agreed.

The outcome wasn't a happy one for Harry. Not only did the tests reveal that he was grossly anaemic and required an urgent blood transfusion, it also transpired that he had severe diabetes. Within days, with considerable reluctance, he had been admitted to hospital but a bed on a female ward must have proved a great trial for him.

Despite everyone's best efforts it was no surprise that he barely lived for another year. He became an insulin-dependent diabetic and it was a constant battle to get him to adhere to a diet. Time, illness and increasing age had taken their toll and, quite frankly, Harry simply lost the will to live and gave up the struggle.

For over a year Rose Cottage lay even more neglected and the boat by then was barely visible. The day came, however, when new people arrived to transform and stamp their own mark on it. But, to me, it was always Harry's place.

Emergency First Aid

I suspect that there are few nurses who relish the thought of having to administer emergency first aid outside of a clinical environment and I definitely fell into that category. Therefore, my heart plummeted one morning when a man banged agitatedly on the window of my car just as I was about to drive off from a patient's house.

"Come quickly, Sister. Someone's collapsed outside Lenny's store."

"Right," I said, in what I hoped was a calm, unhurried manner. "Pop round to the surgery and ask for one of the doctors to attend, while I go and see what I can do."

Trying to give a reasonable impersonation of Roger Bannister breaking the four minute mile, I sped off.

Outside the village emporium a crowd of onlookers had gathered like carrion birds round a corpse. "It's OK, Sister's here," said a woman's voice, whereupon the knot of people respectfully drew back to allow me access to the scene.

Lying motionless on the pavement was a heap of ragged, assorted clothes with a head at one end and boot-shod feet at the other. The bundle seemed to be held together with twine around the middle. Kneeling beside the figure it soon became clear that I was face to face with a tramp. His face was grimy, lined and weather-beaten and the presenting ear had to be the dirtiest I had seen, probably capable of growing seeds in. Furthermore, there were no signs of respirations nor could I feel a pulse. Shoving my hand under the shabby coat and numerous jumpers I managed to detect the faintest of irregular heart beats. Around me stood an audience clearly expecting me to emulate a life-saving drama as shown on television, but I literally recoiled at the thought of trying to give him the 'kiss of life'.

Nevertheless, something had to be done so I made a few pathetic attempts at cardiac massage and after a few good thumps to the chest, to my amazement and the wonder of the assembled throng, the bundle of humanity suddenly emitted a juddering gasp. Praying fervently that he would just keep it up I breathed a sigh of relief as Dr. Chase appeared beside me bearing a cylinder of oxygen and a mask, which he firmly clapped to the face of the casualty whilst supporting his chin.

"What happened?" he asked quietly.

"I'm not really sure," I replied in an equally low voice. "He apparently collapsed quite suddenly and I think he's had a heart attack. He wasn't breathing when I arrived but I simply couldn't face doing 'mouth to mouth'. His ears are absolutely filthy."

Without taking his eyes off of the slowly responding 'gentleman-of-the-road' he murmured: "I've got news for you, Sister. You give the 'kiss of life' via the mouth, not the earhole!"

Mercifully, I was spared the need to respond by the urgent clanging bell of an ambulance drawing up and we thankfully relinquished our charge into the capable hands of the crew. Dr. Chase scribbled some hasty notes and handed them over and we retreated to the surgery for a cup of coffee.

Needless to say the doctor concerned wasted no time in informing all and sundry that his practice possessed the only District Nurse to administer aural resuscitation as opposed to the oral route.

I'm never going to live this one down I thought ruefully. However, a couple of weeks later he greeted me, waving a hospital discharge letter in his hand.

"You remember our tramp?"

"I do, only too well! Please don't tell me he's moving into our territory," I groaned.

"No, but our revered colleagues at the hospital felt that I would like to hear what the final diagnosis was," he said, "and you are not going to believe this."

"Cerebral vascular accident, cardiac myopathy?" I hazarded.

"Nowhere near close," he grinned. "Apparently he was constipated! They have given him a de-coke and sent him on his way rejoicing."

"What?" I choked in disbelief.

"I agree. He may well have been constipated but it was secondary to whatever caused his collapse."

"Perhaps, in future, we should try the anal route for resuscitation," I ventured slyly.

"Well, you and I are clearly worse than useless in the eyes of the hospital staff," he concluded wryly.

A Lonely Old Maid

Doctors' surgery sessions in the 1970s were literally on a first-come first-served basis and continued until the last person had been seen. There were always two doctors in attendance whilst the third set out to undertake the house calls. Everything stopped at eleven o'clock for coffee when the team came together, the receptionist would detail any further requests for home visits and these would be allocated. Morning surgery then continued, usually finishing at about one o'clock and reconvening at five o'clock. Patients would be given either a red or white disc by the receptionist with a number written on it and would sit to wait their turn.

There were the inevitable surgery habitués who turned up with unfailing regularity. One such was Lily Brown who could almost be guaranteed a place at the head of the queue every Monday evening. She was a rather sad, pathetic character, of limited intelligence, and had spent her entire life in service as a lady's maid at the beck and call of others. She vacillated between the doctors, according to which one was in favour with her at the time. However, on no account would she ever agree to see Dr. Standish. He had dealt with Lily for many years and finally told her, what everyone knew, that there was nothing wrong with her and kindly not to waste his time. The only effect this had was to put the onus onto the other two partners who weren't quite as abrupt and forthright.

When the young and unendingly patient Dr. Rivers joined the practice Lily was in her element. Here was a fresh ear into which she could pour the endless list of her steadily increasing symptoms and problems. After the first encounter she returned to the receptionist full of praise for the newcomer. To Jane's amusement and for the information of the rest of the waiting room she announced triumphantly: "He's really lovely and a proper doctor. He's right thorough. Gave me a real good going over, listened to my chest and everything. And he's going to take some blood for testing. Says I'm a real mystery!"

Occasionally the doctors would suggest that she went to see the nurse for any checks that I could do which would keep her happy. I monitored her blood pressure, updated her tetanus, checked her breasts for lumps and bumps, weighed her and discussed her diet, but that ploy didn't last for long.

Week after week Dr. Rivers would patiently sit through Lily's latest saga of woe. However, the day came when he went off on a fortnight's holiday. Arriving promptly at five o'clock the receptionists had to break the news to Lily.

"Perhaps you'd like to see the locum doctor who is standing in for him?" they suggested.

Lily's cup of happiness was full. Here was yet another person to whom she could pour out all her baffling troubles. The only thing was that they failed to mention the name of the relief doctor. Her number was duly called and she trotted off eagerly into the consulting room, only to come to an abrupt halt when confronted by the recently retired Dr. Standish.

"Good evening Lily. Have you got anything worthwhile to tell me because if not, clear off."

Without even sitting down she scuttled back to the desk.

"I'll wait until Dr. Rivers is back," she said.

"He's away for two weeks," the receptionists warned.

"That doesn't matter," she muttered, "I'll wait," and shot out through the door

"So much for being ill," said Jane. "Apparently Lily can tell in advance when she's going to need a doctor."

"The trouble is," I mused, "one of these days there really will be something wrong and none of us are going to believe her."

Every practice had its malingerers and hypochondriacs, which meant that the staff needed the patience of Job.

Unbelievably Double-Jointed

In the '70s there were no such thing as Practice Nurses and the District Nurse undertook both functions. Every Monday and Friday I ran a surgery session for the 'walking wounded' in an attempt to cut down on the number of house calls we were making. For those who lived very locally it was ideal, but with public transport being so infrequent and ill-timed it only partly solved the problem.

As this service became more established patients would often make an appointment with the nurse in case there was no need to see a doctor. That is how I first made contact with Kelly who came in, hopping on one foot, accompanied by her father. She was 11 years old, small and slim, but quite attractive in an elfin kind of way.

"Oh dear," I said as I indicated for her to sit down, "what have you been up to?"

"I've hurt my toe," she offered in a whisper.

"Well, let's have a look, shall we?" So saying, I removed a cheap, black, patent leather shoe and a stained sock. Wrapped around the big toe was a plaster wet with exudate which I gently removed and then stared perplexed at the offending digit. The whole toe was white and looked as though it had been immersed in water for a long time, while the area around the nail was discharging. The general effect was that of Camembert cheese.

"Good heavens," I commented, "whatever caused this?"

She gave a somewhat guilty giggle and cast an eye in her Dad's direction, but nothing was forthcoming.

"Are you going to tell Sister, or shall I?" he asked.

In a shame-faced whisper, she said, "I've been sucking my toe."

My mind reeled. For someone who finds it hard enough to rest a foot on a knee, the thought of actually getting it up to my mouth was mind boggling.

"You may well stare, Sister. The thing is that Kelly is double-jointed and she first started toe-sucking as a baby. We thought she'd grow out of it but she didn't, so the wife resorted to various things like painting it with bitter aloes and mustard. But she actually likes it, would you credit?"

"She can't have been sucking it non-stop for 11 years," I exclaimed.

"No, she stopped when the toe was bandaged each night. There have been one or two lapses but we thought she'd got over it. Because she now baths herself and such like, we've had no cause to see her feet recently. It's only because she started limping that this has come to light."

"Is it just the right toe?" I asked.

"Yes, always the right," her Dad replied.

"Well Kelly, you must be something of a contortionist, I'll give you that."

"I'm quite good at athletics and gymnastics," she smiled. "They're my favourite subjects."

"I don't think you'll be able to get a degree in toe-sucking," I ventured. "However, I'm going to have to ask the doctor to come and look at this."

"Can't you just dress it?" her father asked.

"To be quite frank, I think Kelly's going to need a referral to hospital."

"Hospital!" he exclaimed.

"You see, I think she's in danger of losing that toe nail and it will probably be better to have it surgically removed."

The doctor agreed and within days the procedure was carried out under a nerve block and Kelly came back to the surgery for dressings until it had healed.

"I don't know how we're going to stop this happening again, that's the problem," her mother said on her final visit.

"I've got two suggestions to make," I said. "First, do what they used to do in the trenches during the First World War and have regular foot inspections. Secondly, get some different shoes. Like all synthetic products, plastic and patent don't allow the feet to breathe so there's more chance that they will become sweaty and soggy."

I don't think I was at all popular with Kelly who, like many young girls, apparently treasured all things fashionable but highly unsuitable in the footwear department. However, she had now cooked her goose. It was probably the thought of facing the rest of her life unable to wear the status shoes so loved by her contemporaries that actually solved the problem and stopped a frankly unbelievable habit.

'Goodbye My Darling'

Kevin was a fairly diminutive little boy of four with a history of iron deficiency anaemia. This often manifests itself by abnormal developmental performance, poor growth and increased susceptibility to infection. The condition can be reversed by early iron supplementation orally but, when a patient fails to respond to this treatment, it is sometimes necessary to administer the iron by a course of deep intramuscular injections.

Whenever possible I preferred to treat small children in their home environment, particularly if the procedure was likely to cause distress. A child can all too easily come to associate visits to a surgery with pain and discomfort. Moreover, it is never pleasant for patients in the waiting area to have to listen to screams and wails coming from the treatment room.

Many adults find such injections unpleasant, so I was not surprised that I became anything but popular with young Kevin. When my car pulled up outside the house he would invariably be waiting at the window, and his little voice could be heard proclaiming in desperation, "Mummy, Daddy, the 'prick lady's' here, the 'prick lady's' here." Distressed he undoubtedly was, and it didn't do much for my own self-esteem either.

The father was particularly good at handling his small son and I soon came to learn that Kevin was quite a good mimic. His favourite subject at the time was the comedian Charlie Drake who, with his blond, curly hair and childlike manner, was known nationally for his catchphrase: "Hello, my darlings." However, there was no way that this little boy was ever going to greet me with such affection.

One of his much loved renditions was the song 'Mr. Custer', redolent with flying arrows and Red Indian whoops and war cries. Consequently, it became customary to be greeted by a little lad wearing an American Cavalry Officer's hat, saying: "Please Mr. Custer, I don't want to go," or "Please Mr. Custer, can I be excused now?" Without doubt, I was the unacceptable face of authority.

On a chart on the wall, Kevin had been marking off the number of nursing visits to be made. On the final day he triumphantly scored a line through the date and actually beamed from ear to ear.

"Haven't you got something to say to Sister?" his father prompted.

Looking me straight in the eye, and giving his best Charlie Drake imitation, he said, "Goodbye, my darling," and I was triumphantly shown the door.

Burns

More distressing still are the cases involving even younger children or babies.

Melanie was only 16 months and the child of an inexperienced first-time mum. Their house was brand new and every attention had been paid to ensure the safety of the active toddler. There were safety gates on the stairs, safety devices on the cupboard doors, a guard rail along the front of the cooker and a fireguard in front of the open fire. Nevertheless, it only took one thoughtless act to leave a young mother absolutely racked with guilt and her steadily growing confidence in tatters.

It was late winter and the days were still chilly, but Fiona didn't bother to light the fire in the lounge till after lunch. Melanie still went in her cot for a sleep mid-morning so, once she was dressed and breakfasted, she played on the floor in the kitchen which was heated by an electric wall heater, while the mother got on with the chores.

One morning a neighbour came round for a chat and Fiona decided to put a portable electric fire in the lounge so that they could sit in comfort. As there were only the two of them the fireguard wasn't erected. When Melanie woke up her mother brought her downstairs. She turned the fire off and stood the child on the floor while she went to get her a drink. The heater had sturdy wires across the front protecting the elements but it was only too easy for a tiny hand to find a way in to investigate. Although the appliance was switched off and the bars no longer glowing red they still possessed a searing heat.

Melanie's heart-rending screams brought Fiona running, only to find that her precious child had actually grasped hold of one of the elements. The damage done to tender young flesh can only be imagined. Mother and child found themselves resident on the burns unit at East Grinstead until the skin grafts had taken and she was considered well enough to return to the care of the District Nurse for daily dressings and a regime of passive exercises to prevent contractures of the hand.

It wasn't a procedure which I enjoyed as I felt deeply for both mother and child in their obvious distress.

Anyone For Fondue?

Busily trying to wade through the seemingly endless number of people wanting to see the nurse at the Monday evening surgery session, I was quite unprepared for the spectacle which Michael Tandridge presented. The receptionist had discreetly ushered him through to the examination room, ahead of the queue. He was a tall, good-looking man in his early fifties, but what marked him out from the rest of the surgery patients was the fact that he was wearing pyjamas and a dressing gown. His face was contorted with pain and his wife fluttered anxiously by his side.

"We've been on a skiing holiday in Switzerland. We popped back home first, so Mike could get into something looser, otherwise we would have come here straight from the airport," she said apologetically

"What's the problem?" I asked.

Untying the cord he allowed the pyjama bottoms to fall to the ground along with some large pieces of non-adhesive gauze dressings. From knee to groin and beyond was a bright red, excoriated, weeping area. His discomfort was only too clear.

"Let's get you on the couch," I said swiftly.

Painfully he swung himself up then lay back with relief as I brought the angle-poise lamp to bear on the situation and removed the remaining dressings. In the glare of the light it looked even worse. Not only were both thighs involved but the scrotum and penis and bottom of the abdomen as well.

"Would one of you like to tell me what happened?"

"Last evening we were enjoying a meal in the hotel restaurant with eight friends to celebrate the final night of our holiday. We all decided to have a fondue. After we finished a local folk group played and we started to sing. Some of us began to thump the table in time to the music. The table was wooden but highly polished and none of us saw the fondue set creeping near the edge as a result of the vibrations. The next thing I knew the container of boiling oil had spilled into my lap," he groaned.

"What did the hospital do?" I asked.

"I didn't go to one. Our flight was leaving in the morning and I didn't want to miss it. I got the bottom half of me under a cold shower while the chaps went off into the town and managed to find a store open where they purchased these dressings and some bandages."

"You must have been in agony," I exclaimed rather pointlessly.

"Still am, for that matter. I keep swallowing the wife's Panadol but they don't seem to be doing much good."

Placing a modesty sheet lightly across the area I hastily left to ask one of the doctors to come and have a look.

"You've made a terrific job of that Mike," said Dr. Chase peering over his half-glasses. "What do you think Sister?"

"My first instinct was to send him straight to casualty," I replied.

"No, I don't want to go to hospital, please," he begged.

"And your second thought?" the doctor continued.

"If you look closely, I don't think the skin is involved to the degree I first thought it was."

Bending down he peered closely again, then finally stood upright.

"Shall we give it a go?" he asked.

"I'm prepared to try, but only with the proviso that I am at liberty to change my mind the minute I'm not happy."

"There you are Mike, can't say fairer than that," the doctor said.

"Write out the prescriptions you will require for dressings Sister and I'll sign them. I'll also include a stronger painkiller and an antibiotic to provide cover against the risk of infection. Then, if you pop round to the chemist and collect them," he said, addressing the wife, "Sister will attend to the wound now and arrange with you about daily dressings."

Turning back, he said, "I don't imagine you'll find it very pleasant passing urine for a while."

"Tell me something I don't already know," Michael grimaced.

"Well, any troubles in that department and I want to be told immediately."

Amazingly, no difficulties were encountered and it afforded me great satisfaction to see the steady improvement. Initially the daily dressing procedures were something of an endurance test but he was a resilient chap and rarely complained. Finally, the day came when he was able to immerse himself in a bath and within six weeks he was pronounced healed, although the skin remained discoloured. Nevertheless, his crown jewels had been restored to their former glory.

Fondue would remain permanently excluded from that gentleman's menu in the future for the memories were too painful.

Slain By A Breast

Of all surgical procedures there is probably none more shattering for a woman than a mastectomy. The feelings engendered by the seeming loss of femininity, coupled with the emotional fallout and the possibility of the cancer becoming a life sentence, are huge.

Maggie Sewell was an attractive woman of 50, happily married with two grown-up daughters now living in the nearby town. Her council house was immaculate and the large garden a joy to behold.

Tragedy struck on the day she became aware of a lump in her left breast. There were no screening facilities available then, so by the time a lump had been detected the cancer was often well-advanced. This proved to be the case with Maggie and when she presented herself at the hospital it had spread to the lymph nodes. Thus she was forced to undergo a radical mastectomy.

The surgeon concerned was extremely competent but noted more for the enthusiasm of his surgery than the final cosmetic effect. Therefore, when Dr. Standish asked me to visit and dress the wound I was quite prepared for what I would find. The S-shaped incision was irregular and heavily scored across the skin. This was his trademark method of matching up the sides of the wound when suturing. The result meant that the patient resembled a piece of slashed pork rind until all was healed. In Maggie's case that was going to take some time, as there were three areas on the incision line that were slightly gaping following the removal of the stitches.

On my first visit I found Maggie sitting listlessly in an armchair in her pristine sitting room. Her whole attitude resembled that of someone who has had the stuffing completely knocked out of them. Her greeting was friendly enough but totally lacklustre.

"Don't ask me to look at it, Sister because I just can't bear to," she said. Gently I removed the dressing whilst she carefully averted her eyes.

"What do you think?" she asked anxiously.

"Don't worry, I've seen worse," I assured her with scant regard for the truth. "It will take a week or so but we'll get there."

Painstakingly I cleaned and redressed the wound and strapped the dressing in place. Once done, Maggie put on her bra, stuffed some handkerchiefs into the empty cup and pulled on her blouse.

There were no specialist breast nurses in hospitals back then and any practical and psychological support was down to the staff involved. Over the next few days I quickly recognised that Maggie's journey towards recovery and acceptance of her condition had a long way to go.

"Have they said anything about providing a prosthesis?" I asked.

"What?" she queried.

"An artificial breast."

"I've been measured and they said they'd send it in the post. It should be here within a couple of weeks."

"Right," I said determinedly, "that gives us a goal to work towards, doesn't it?"

"I suppose so," she said morosely.

Slowly progress was made but two areas stubbornly refused to dry up completely. It was a brilliant summer that year and one day I asked Maggie if she was prepared to try something a little unconventional.

"What's that Sister?"

"Have you got a lounger? I asked.

"Yes," she replied in bemusement.

"Well, I think that this wound could do with being exposed to the air and sunlight. I've noticed that there's an ideal spot in your back garden behind the shed. There's a high hedge on one side and because you're on a corner plot it's not overlooked. How about giving it a try?"

"If you think it will help I'll have a go," she said dubiously.

She was soon comfortably ensconced on the lounger with a cold drink, a book and sunglasses.

"Just imagine you're on the Costa Brava," I suggested. For the first time I heard a slight laugh. "I'll be back in a couple of hours to replace the dressing. If by any chance anyone comes, just put your blouse across your chest."

When I returned I found her fast asleep.

"Do you know sister, that was lovely," she admitted after I had gently roused her.

Once back in the house, I replaced the dressing. Observing her carefully I remarked: "You're actually looking the most relaxed I've seen you yet. Shall we have another session tomorrow?"

She readily agreed and I volunteered to come mid-morning so that the sunbathing time could be extended. "If you want to come indoors for any reason, just pop your blouse on for a moment."

By the end of the week the wound was healed.

"Would you like a drink Sister?" It was the first time that Maggie had made any such gesture.

"Oh, that would be heaven. You'd better make it coffee rather than gin though."

"As if," she laughed.

With biscuits and coffee on the table, I decided it was as good a time as any to start probing with some gentle questions.

"Do you know Maggie, during the time I've known you, you've never once asked me any questions or told me how you are really feeling."

"What's there to ask or tell?" she shrugged.

"Plenty, I imagine. I know I would if I were in your shoes."

"The one thing that's worrying me is the thought of having radiotherapy," she sighed.

"It's another big hurdle, I admit, but I think you'll find the reality much less frightening than the thoughts you are now harbouring. You won't be on your own because I will be with you every step of the way and if there are any unpleasant side effects we'll be able to help with suitable remedies. But don't even start to cross that bridge until you actually come to it. You may well find that you are worrying needlessly."

There was a pause before I asked: "Will someone be going with you Maggie?"

"I don't know," she muttered.

"What about the family?"

"I haven't discussed anything with them," she interposed hastily.

"Not even your husband?" I persisted.

"No, I simply can't," she stated flatly. "I don't want to talk about it and I've told them so."

"Maggie, they all love you to bits. Don't you think that they're worried too and are desperate to be able to do something to help? By pushing them away you aren't being kind to yourself or to them."

"I just don't feel a woman anymore," she moaned. "I can't even let Mick hold me because who'd really want to cuddle a nonentity?"

"Good heavens Maggie, you've lost a breast not your looks or personality. Tell him how you feel. You've every right to be angry, sad and depressed. All those things are completely normal and many people in your position face the same problems, but it's far, far easier if you don't try to go it alone. Don't you think he'll understand?"

"I just don't know about anything any more," she sighed.

The conversation was cut short by a knock at the door. It was a parcel post delivery with a hospital label. She tore it open to reveal a box inside which nestled the breast prosthesis. Holding it in her hand Maggie looked at me in near despair.

"It weighs a ton, and how on earth am I supposed to fit this in a bra?"

"Go and get a clean bra," I suggested, "and we'll have a look."

Specialist providers of mastectomy bras did not yet exist, but I explained that all that was required was a piece of material stitched like a pocket to the inside of the cup with an opening in which to insert the artificial breast.

"See what you can manage and I'll pop in tomorrow and check."

The following day was a Saturday. I entered the kitchen as usual and came face to face with a man sitting at the kitchen table sporting the biggest black eye I'd seen in a long time.

"This is my husband," Maggie explained.

"Goodness," I exclaimed, "have you been in a fight?"

"I suppose you could say so, Sister," he smiled ruefully and they both laughed.

Sensing a considerable lightening of the atmosphere I said, "Whatever happened?"

"After you'd gone yesterday, I got my machine out and sewed a pocket in my bra. I fitted the 'thingy' and decided to wear it to try and get used to it," Maggie explained.

Mick took up the story. "When we went upstairs last night, Mags sat on the bed to get undressed. Her back was to me and the light off, as she has insisted on doing ever since she came home from hospital."

Maggie started to giggle. "I undid my bra like I usually do and went to toss it on the chair completely forgetting that it was weighted down on one side. As I swung it round it caught Mick in the eye."

"I'm not kidding you Sister, it was like being sandbagged," he grimaced.

"Well, you're not far wrong in your assessment of the contents," I grinned.

At that time, prosthetic breasts possessed none of the lightweight, aesthetic qualities of the later silicone models.

Quite fortuitously, the incident broke the ice for this couple and helped her come to terms with her loss. Now she was able to communicate her feelings and permit her husband to share her pain and grief. They became once more a happy, loving family unit where there were no secrets and no one felt excluded. She weathered the radiotherapy effortlessly with every support from her family. I would sometimes meet them out shopping and they invariably reminded me of the flying breast incident with hilarity.

The survival rates then for women undergoing radical mastectomy for breast cancer were nowhere near as good as the prognosis for sufferers today in the 21st century. I don't think any of us were surprised when Maggie developed secondaries in her lungs two years later and died within two months.

It was not only the diversity of problems presented by the general public who beat a path to the surgery which made the role of the District Nurse so interesting. There was also the privilege of treating them in the intimate surroundings of their own homes, sharing in the hopes, triumphs and heartbreaks, not only of the patients but their families as well.

Chapter Four. Primitive Facilities

 I have to confess that prior to my career as a nurse I hadn't given much, if any, consideration to domestic sanitary arrangements. However, thanks to the sometimes questionable human plumbing system, within days of commencing training, I rapidly became acquainted with the relentless bodily functions of my patients, requiring the provision of urinals and bedpans. The contents of these swiftly disappeared, courtesy of the wonderful invention of a bedpan steriliser.

A subsequent visit to a waterworks and a sewage plant was deemed a necessary part of a nurse's education, although I rapidly dismissed it as interesting if fairly irrelevant. Never having lived anywhere other than the genteel environs of suburban Surrey, all mod cons were taken for granted.

After only a matter of weeks on the District I was forced to seriously reconsider the matter, as I encountered a seemingly incredible number of patients whose lives were governed by regular trips down the garden in all weathers. The china chamber pot usually did service at night, or if conditions were particularly inclement. Primitive, irritating and unsavoury as their sanitary arrangements were, I had given no thought regarding the final disposal of the end products until I met Mr. King.

Percy and his wife lived with a daughter in single-storey prefab accommodation on the outskirts of my village and in fairly close proximity to the sewage plant. He was the most delightful man, quiet and self-effacing. I first knew him as a regular member of the church congregation, where he was also a keen and experienced bell-ringer.

The day came when his elderly wife began to succumb to a long-standing, chronic heart condition and the District Nurses were called in to offer care and support. The Kings were a very close family and they clearly felt deeply for the old lady. The home was spick and span, the garden lovingly tended and nothing was too much trouble for them to provide or do.

Spending as much time with such patients as we did, it was almost inevitable that there would be some reminiscing. The nurses often gleaned information about their patients' lives, and fascinating snippets of local history, which is how I came upon the story of the Lavender Wagon.

In the 19th century, when the majority of homes had outside facilities in the shape of pail closets, thunder-boxes, privy middens and cesspools, it was the Local Authority who was responsible for emptying these. Under the cover of darkness, the 'night soil men' would collect the contents weekly and load them into a horse-drawn wooden cart which, not unsurprisingly, stank to high heaven. They would then be disposed of on a dump outside the village at dawn, or delivered to farms to be spread on the land. The carts were nicknamed Lavender Wagons and Percy had been the local driver until well after the war.

In time, council vehicles appeared with more sophisticated means of dealing with some of these offerings, but there were still many of my patients who were obliged to make their own disposal arrangements, usually by digging a hole and burying the excreta. Often the prize exhibits at flower and vegetable shows owed their success to this particular method of manuring rather than the skill of the grower.

As sanitation improved, Percy's dumping ground eventually became the local sewage farm and he relinquished what I considered to be a labour of love above and beyond the call of duty. Over time chemical closets made their appearance and how many 'thunder-boxes' and earth closets still exist, if any, I have absolutely no idea. Nevertheless, in the '70s and '80s they still loomed large on my horizon.

In An Emergency, Ask The Vicar!

The Dodds were something of a ménage-à-trois without the sexual connotations. Jacob and his wife Eva were well into their late eighties and of quite comfortably solid proportions. They lived in a late Victorian cottage set in a fair-sized garden which had largely run to seed, except for the odd patches showing signs of recent attempts at cultivation.

Jacob's younger spinster sister, Jessie, lived with them and was the complete antithesis. A tiny, bird-like creature with brown, pebbly eyes accentuated by thick glasses, she was virtually incapable of holding a conversation, preferring instead to nod or shake her head vigorously depending on what her brother or sister-in-law said. She had an extremely irritating, silly little cough which constantly punctuated the proceedings. Generally she was a jumpy bundle of nerves.

I was asked to visit them after Dr. Rivers had found them in a pitiful state. Eva and Jessie were both in bed with bronchitis verging on pneumonia. Jacob, who was similarly affected, was valiantly trying to hold things together but had been dispatched upstairs to join his wife.

Once again I was faced with a house which possessed no bathroom or inside toilet. In this case the privy was halfway down the garden. It never ceased to amaze me just how many homes still existed with the most primitive of facilities. Straightaway, I collected two commodes from Nursing Towers and crammed them into the back of the car. No one had ever warned me that the skills of a removal firm would be needed for the job. There was a weekly delivery service from central stores, several miles distant, which was fine if your patient could wait but unsatisfactory in an emergency.

I will never forget the look of sheer gratitude on the faces of Jacob, Eva and Jessie when I provided what for them was sheer luxury. Needless to say, there was no running hot water but two kettles lived on the range in the living room and this was sufficient to carry out their daily toiletry care.

The next thing to be addressed was the matter of nourishment, once again solved through the goodness and generosity of neighbours. Some time previously I had delivered a baby at a nearby house and now approached the mother to ask whether she thought there were any folk around who would be able to help.

"Don't give it another thought Sister. I can rustle up enough people and we'll do it on a rota system."

Expressing my gratitude I assured her that simple soups, jellies and custards would be quite sufficient. Between them this little community visited three times a day to provide hot drinks and to stoke the range to keep it going. Meanwhile I visited every morning to administer general care and empty the commodes in the garden.

The three of them were suffering quite badly from chest infections and for a while it was touch and go whether Jessie would require hospital admission. Fortunately, this was averted and, one by one, I managed to get them rehabilitated and back downstairs. Seated round a table with them one day, I suggested that they would now be capable of washing and dressing themselves to which they readily agreed. Eva, however, became quite agitated.

"You won't be taking the commodes away will you Sister?"

Smilingly I assured her that they would remain and that I would drop in at some time during the day to empty them until Jacob was able to go outdoors and do it for them.

After expressing their thanks the married couple began to open up and fill me in with snippets of their life story.

"Lived here all my life I have. Went to the village school, sang in the church choir and, until a few years ago, I used to ring the bells," Jacob informed me proudly. "Once I couldn't ride my bike though it was no good 'cos it's too far to walk."

Eva nodded in agreement, whilst Jessie punctuated every sentence with her irritating cough. "She can't help it," Eva whispered loudly, "it's her nerves you see."

At which they all gravely nodded.

"Do you have any visitors?" I enquired.

"Not really because all our old friends are virtually housebound like us, and there's no close family left now. We talk to the neighbours if we're in the garden and happen to see them," said the older pair. "Our groceries are delivered each week and the butcher and the milkman call."

"The vicar used to come," said Jacob, "but he's gone. Used to enjoy chatting to him, didn't we Eva?"

"There's a new one now." I replied. "Would you like him to visit perhaps?"

"He won't want to be bothered with the likes of us Sister."

"I'm sure he will and if I see him, I'll ask."

Once again three heads nodded their assent.

Later that day I happened to bump into the said gentleman coming out of the chemist and I relayed the saga.

"Of course I'll call. Say no more and consider it done," he responded cheerfully.

That night I was up with a confinement, which duly curtailed all my visits the following day. Consequently it was almost teatime when I finally reached the Dodds to empty the commodes. I found them literally bubbling with excitement.

"He's just been Sister, the new vicar, and he's right nice."

Jessie's head wobbled frantically in agreement.

"That's wonderful," I replied.

"And he's coming again and he might even be able to get someone to fetch me so I can go and hear the bells," Jacob eagerly informed me.

"Well, I'll just go and get the commodes then."

"Oh, you needn't bother, Sister; we got the vicar to do it."

I'm sure my face must have been a picture, as I conjured up the thought of that young man trundling down to the privy with the freewill offerings of his parishioners.

Sure enough, when I next saw him he had something to say on the subject.

"Well, thanks to you, pastoral visiting has assumed a whole new meaning," he said ruefully. "I wasn't quite prepared for commodes. Somehow they didn't feature in my theological training."

"Never mind," I grinned, "to your eternal credit you did it."

"Yes I did, but I hope it won't be a regular requirement," he added with considerable feeling.

Yet again the value of true community spirit had been proved.

Emergency Evacuation

The very nature of nursing inevitably necessitates getting up close and personal with some people who, given the choice, you'd frankly rather keep at a reasonable distance. Not surprisingly, in these cases, any willing participation by the community was never going to be forthcoming.

Jed Thorne was a reclusive character of indeterminate age and somewhat unprepossessing appearance. He was a familiar figure as he cycled through the village, en route to the coast, on a heavy, old-fashioned bicycle which looked as though it had done service in the war. His attire, whatever the weather, consisted of a fawn raincoat belted at the waist, worn over unremarkable trousers, the bottoms held in place with cycle clips. However, his unmistakable trademark was the thick plait of dark and greasy, matted hair hanging down his back, adding a piratical look to his general unsavoury air.

Apart from a brief exchange of words with the shopkeepers, he was a totally private person and never attempted to engage in conversation with anyone else. In his younger days he had worked on a smallholding abutting the surrounding orchards and the family home. Both had fallen into a state of neglect, since when his days

90

were mostly spent foraging among the flotsam and jetsam found along the seashore, like some ardent beachcomber.

His small Victorian brick cottage had originally been built by his grandfather. On his death the son moved in and here Jed had been brought up, along with three sisters. One married and moved to a neighbouring village whilst the second daughter occupied a nearby house of wooden construction with her husband. The youngest child was mentally retarded and, on the death of the parents, was taken next door to be cared for by her sister, leaving Jed on his own. Assorted relatives lived scattered around the area, but there appeared to be no interaction between them. They all kept themselves very much to themselves. Procreation certainly hadn't been high on their agendas for most remained childless, which was probably a mercy. Similarly, many had chosen not to avail themselves of even the most modest sanitary improvements, which meant their living conditions remained archaic to say the least.

The never-to-be-forgotten day arrived when an apologetic Dr. Chase requested the District Nurses to visit Jed for the purpose of administering an enema.

"He can't remember when he last functioned. I've done a rectal examination and his bowel is clearly loaded but it's very high up. See what you can do for him. Oh, you'd better take a commode with you," was his parting shot as he exited the room at speed.

Casting a meaningful look towards the Enrolled Nurse I said, "I think this is one visit that will be better accomplished double-handed."

Both receptionists watched sympathetically as we assembled everything we thought we might possibly need before setting off to meet yet another challenge.

Patients requiring relief from constipation when all aperients had failed were not at all uncommon in the '70s. This was partly a legacy of previous generations who regarded inner cleanliness to be an essential part of general hygiene. If soap and water was necessary to ensure freshness of the skin, then something must be ingested that would guarantee equal purity of the parts that couldn't be seen.

Consequently, the weekly bath night invariably meant the ritual administration of some nauseous concoction to aid the matter. Many patients related tales of being dosed from childhood with mixtures ranging from treacle and brimstone, Epsom Salts, infusion of Senna Pods and Cascara through to relatively gentle Syrup of Figs and Milk of Magnesia, regardless of whether they were needed or not.

It is almost inevitable that such unnecessary assaults on the intestinal tract would eventually have an effect on the natural workings of the bowel over time. As a result, the administration of enemas was quite a commonplace part of the District Nurses work when glycerine suppositories and all other methods had failed.

An enema is the procedure of introducing liquids into the rectum and colon via the anus in order to create powerful peristaltic movement which will result in complete evacuation of the lower bowel. Once considered a favourite fashionable medical treatment amongst Western nobility, they also had a long history of use in midwifery to induce labour.

Good, old-fashioned soap and water was the general standby, administered via a catheter, funnel and rubber tubing, accompanied by the mantra 'high, hot and a hell of a lot'! However, this method has largely fallen out of use because of its irritating chemical reaction on the mucosa, as well as the ready availability of other preparations that are equally effective but often kinder and easier to administer. Many self-administered, disposable enemas are now packaged for home use which thankfully has relieved the need for intervention by the District Nurse. However, we were not so fortunate then.

On our arrival it was evident that Fairview Cottage certainly lived up to its name externally, but we soon discovered that the interior presented a very different picture. Preparing to enter by the back door I caught sight of the well and had a horrible feeling of what awaited us.

The kitchen was spartan but reasonably clean. A fire was alight in an old-fashioned range which ran along one wall. On top was a kettle and a cast iron pot, the contents of which were bubbling gently. Below a small window, looking out onto the orchards, was a shallow stone sink, but without any taps. Instead, standing sentinel beside the sink, was a pump from which protruded a handle and spout. On a small wooden table was an old-fashioned oil lamp. A glance to the ceiling revealed the absence of any light fittings. There was no electricity.

Theresa and I were eying each other dubiously when Jed emerged from the living room. Quickly we introduced ourselves, made sure that he knew and understood why we had come, and set about explaining what would be required. Conversation was non-existent, 'yes' and 'no' being his only words.

"We shall need some hot water, Jed," I continued.

Jerking his head in the direction of the kitchen in an expressionless voice he said: "Kettle's on the stove."

"Can you tell me where the toilet is?" I questioned, already guessing the answer.

"Down the garden," came the reply.

"In which case we're going to need a commode," I said with a brightness I was far from feeling.

Theresa headed out to fetch the said article from the car. I couldn't help thinking that a missionary in darkest Africa in the 19th century was hardly worse equipped. However, a Bible was the least of my requirements at that moment.

"Jed, we will need to have you lying on your side on the bed," I informed him.

Without a word he set off toward the stairs with Theresa and I struggling behind with our impedimenta. Our footsteps echoed hollowly on the bare boards which continued along a short landing and into an unbelievably basic and unadorned bedroom. Here we were confronted with a single iron bedstead, but no mattress. Over the springs were several layers of thick cardboard. A couple of grey army blankets were folded over the foot of the bed while two pillows at the other end did at least sport pillowcases. A cane-seated wooden chair stood nearby, on which rested a candle in a candle holder and a box of matches.

For a moment the three of us stood immobile as the scene was surveyed and digested. Eventually I summoned up the voice to enquire whether Jed could provide a sheet.

"No," he replied. "Don't use them 'cos they need washing."

Well, I suppose he had a point. Disposable was clearly best!

While Theresa returned to the kitchen to mix the soap and water for the enema, I set about covering the bed liberally with incontinence sheets before positioning Jed on his side and offering the necessary instructions. The deed was duly performed and we stood waiting for the moment of return. We waited and we waited but Jed remained lying impassively on his side. I had never known anyone retain an enema of that quantity for so long.

This delay in the proceedings did ensure that Theresa and I had ample opportunity to study Jed's tonsorial masterpiece at close range and it wasn't a pretty sight. For how many years this twisted, tightly matted rope of hair had adorned his person was impossible to say, nor could we hazard a guess as to when, if ever, it had been washed. How many unwanted little visitors had infested it over time, only to die incarcerated and turn to dust in the knotted tangle, I dare not surmise. One thing was for sure, it certainly wouldn't attract any self-respecting creatures now.

In the end I was driven to ask: "Jed, do you feel like going to the toilet?"

"No," he mumbled.

"Well, I'd like you to get up and sit on this commode and try," I said. Once settled he was urged to strain down as hard as he could. Back came the soap and water with a gush, and that was it. Clearly our effort had been worse than useless.

"Are you in any pain, Jed?" I asked.

"I'm just uncomfortable because I can't go," he replied.

"Well, I think we need to get hold of Dr. Chase," I said, "because I'm not prepared to repeat this performance without knowing a bit more about what's going on."

It goes without saying that there was no phone and so Theresa was dispatched back to the surgery. Within half an hour she returned with the welcome news that Dr. Chase had facilitated Jed's transfer to the hospital, where the situation could be dealt with more expeditiously and with better cover. The ambulance would be arriving shortly.

"I'm just going to pop along to your sister, to let her know what's happening," I said. "Is that alright Jed?

"Yes," was the monosyllabic reply.

Not without some apprehension I knocked at the door of the wooden house just along the road. It was opened by a motherly little woman, neatly dressed and welcoming.

"Come in Sister. I suppose you've come about our Jed?"

The house was a pleasant surprise. It was clean, warm and homely and clearly showed little feminine touches. The presence of oil lamps indicated that, yet again, here was a property with no electricity. Standing on a small table at the bottom of the box staircase was a 'Wee Willie Winkie' candle holder. However, the stone sink at the kitchen end of the room did at least boast a tap. A basket of washing rested on a chair beside a wooden table covered with a blanket, whilst warming on the top of the range were two old-fashioned flat-irons.

"All this lack of facilities must make an awful lot of work for you," I commented with considerable sympathy.

"We've never known any different Sister and what you haven't had you can't miss," she replied philosophically. "We've had the chance to be connected to the mains and everything but it would mean contributing to the expense, not to mention the payment of bills. This way everything's free except for the coal we use."

I suppose she had a point although the thought of a steadily ageing soul carrying naked candles up the stairs of a wooden building did set alarm bells ringing in my head.

"I'm sorry you've had to try to cope with the situation down the road," she continued. "I do go there and try to sort things out from time to time, but Jed's a law unto himself. Always has been, I'm afraid. He lets me wash his shirts and underwear and occasionally he'll accept a meal I've made but that's about it."

"Well, I'm afraid we've got to send him to hospital but it's nothing serious," I hastened to assure her. "He'll probably only be there for the night."

"Oh Sister, what am I going to do? He's got no pyjamas or anything suitable to take in."

"Don't worry about any of that," I comforted. "The hospital will sort something out for him. In the meantime, however, I would be grateful if you could see what needs to be done in tending to the range and locking the house."

"That's no problem Sister, I'll come directly," she responded.

Jed was duly evacuated from his home, hopefully to be more successfully evacuated in the care of the hospital staff.

Returning to the surgery as dusk descended, we both pondered all that we had witnessed, which only affirmed what we already knew: 'There's none so queer as folks.'

It Defies Belief

It is very hard for a nurse to have to accept that there are occasions when she is able to do little or nothing to relieve a situation and Jed was not the only patient who failed to respond under difficult circumstances.

On an early spring morning in 1975 Dr. Rivers met me as I was about to leave the surgery.

"Sister, I'm afraid I've got a bit of a difficult one for you."

"That sounds ominous," I smiled. "What's the problem?"

Always quiet and never one for small talk or exaggeration, he gave a huge sigh. "A brother and sister in Swavely are living in what I can only describe as putrid circumstances. George is 71, but looks much older and has developed severe bronchitis. He is in bed. I have started him on antibiotics but I'm not convinced that he will take them. He also needs help with his general care because it seems to be beyond the scope of his 69-year-old sister. Would you mind casting your eye over the circumstances to see what's to be done?"

When he had gone, the receptionist said: "Ann, you might find it helpful to have the name and address of another brother and his wife who live nearby."

"Oh Lord," I muttered. "Is it that awful?"

"Obviously," Jane said, "I don't actually know them but I've heard enough." She gave me one of her sympathetic looks.

"Curiouser and curiouser, as Alice said," I replied. "Clearly all is yet to be revealed."

Nothing, though, could ever have prepared me for the scene I encountered.

Despite the name, Main Road Farm was actually on a very minor road and was a solid, grey, early Victorian house, set back from the road in large grounds which had totally gone to seed. The front door was plainly never used so I drove my car along an unmade-up driveway round to the back. There were no signs of life, nor any response to my knock. Gingerly opening the door and preparing to call out, I was forced to stop abruptly and take a deep breath.

I found myself in what presumably was the kitchen although it was impossible to tell for it was strewn with litter. Newspapers, empty bottles, packets and tins, bits of rag and clothing covered the floor and filled every available space, while the all-pervading smell defied description.

There was no reply to my call so I ventured further into a room which was presumably a dining room, but the floor and every chair and surface were similarly covered with debris. A door in one corner revealed a box staircase, already narrow but made worse by the piles of old newspapers on every step. On reaching the landing I called again and heard a faint voice coming from the furthest bedroom. Threading my way past the clutter I entered to find an elderly man huddled under a jumble of indescribably dirty bedding, his head resting on a pillow with only a ticking cover from which feathers were escaping. On a bedside table stood a bottle of water, a glass, and his tablets.

Introducing myself I enquired what I could do to help.

"Nothing, I'm alright," was the response.

"Are you taking your medicine?"

"Yes."

Picking up the bottle I did a quick check on the contents and calculated that the requisite number was missing.

"How are you managing to wash and shave?" I ventured, noting his stubble.

"All right."

"Would you like me to help you?"

"No."

"How are you managing to get any food?"

"Hilda."

"Is that your sister?"

"Yes."

"Do you know where she is?"

"In bed."

"Is she unwell too?"

"No. She's there all day."

Deciding to investigate further I returned to the landing and quietly peered round the open doors. One proved to be a bathroom, although I couldn't imagine when it had last been used or, for that matter, cleaned. There was none of the expected articles visible, save for an extremely grubby towel whose original colour defied recognition. From a mug on the windowsill a pair of ancient dentures stared at me ghoulishly.

Another room revealed an empty bed absolutely piled high with a veritable jumble of articles. Books, old magazines and records mixed up with an assortment of footwear were all strewn over the floor.

The remaining room was in darkness, but from the daylight on the landing it was possible to discern another hump, presumably Hilda, under piles of assorted bedding. The rest of the space was taken up with the same detritus which appeared everywhere else in the house.

Returning to my patient I once more asked whether there was anything he would like or that I could do.

"No."

Exhorting him to be sure to continue taking his tablets and with a promise to call again, I returned downstairs. Once outdoors I drew in great gasps of fresh air. Dr. River's description had proved to be brief to the point of useless, I decided.

Consulting the piece of paper Jane had given me I resolved to pay a visit to George's brother. He and his wife lived in a tiny cottage nearby, with an equally small, but well-tended garden. To my relief, though, it was warm, welcoming, and above all, clean. The aroma of baking which greeted me was an infinite improvement on the one I had just left. Introducing myself I explained the reason for my call.

"I really am very concerned about the situation regarding your brother and sister and wondered whether you would be able to help?"

The man, who bore a striking resemblance to George, cast a look in the direction of his wife before saying: "You'd best come in Sister, I'm Fred."

The story which unfolded was fascinating. Apparently, Main Road Farm formed part of the estate of the late Edward Carpenter who would appear to have been a modest, simple country farmer but a fairly prolific breeder.

Several of his children had already departed this life, leaving Fred and George and two other brothers, Harold and Herbert, who also lived locally with their wives. George had never married and lived with their only sister Hilda, the youngest child, in the original farmhouse. On the death of their father, they were allowed to remain there. The boys continued to farm the land, after a fashion, under the name of Carpenter and Sons.

Later that morning I met the other brothers and quickly deduced that, not only did they resemble three of the dwarfs from Snow White, in features at least if not in stature, none of them were the sharpest knives in the drawer. Unfortunately, George and Hilda were the least capable of this incongruous family.

The three older brothers purported to be ashamed and concerned over the state of the interior of the farmhouse, but seemed incapable of exerting any influence or bringing any pressure to bear on the matter. The main stumbling block appeared to be Hilda who had spent a considerable time incarcerated in the local psychiatric hospital some years ago. However, on the death of the father she returned to the farm, allegedly to look after George. According to Harold, though, her mental state was poor and she suffered from 'moon madness'.

None of them could recall the last time she had washed or changed her clothes. She was an inveterate hoarder and seemed to spend all day in bed and all night roaming around. Any attempts by the brothers or their wives to assist in cleaning the place, providing food or aiding their welfare in any way was met with physical and verbal abuse, which they either wouldn't or couldn't cope with. The only help Hilda would accept was the collection of their weekly pensions and shopping.

"Well," I said, "quite frankly, neither I nor anyone else can provide any sort of care until all that rubbish is cleared."

"Believe me Sister, we'd like to see that above all things," they voiced in unison, "but Hilda won't have it."

"In its present state I consider that it constitutes both a health and a fire risk."

They all nodded vigorously.

"As a result of what I have seen today, I intend to send a report to the Local Health Inspector at the Council asking him to visit. However, I think he will need to speak to you first."

"That's no problem Sister. Just tell him that the three of us work together every afternoon in the old barn at the back of the farm," said Fred.

"And we have a key to get into the house in case it's locked," Herbert volunteered.

Reporting back to Dr. Rivers, I told him in no uncertain terms what I thought.

"To say that you were economical with the truth is an understatement. Not even the most dedicated saint could provide general care in that scenario. I've got feet and hands, not wings, a halo and a magic wand," I declared firmly, much to the amusement of the receptionists.

Outlining the plans to clear the place, I suggested that it would be accomplished with greater ease if he could arrange for George and his bronchitis to be admitted to the elderly care unit at the hospital.

Fortunately, everything fell into place as planned and, having read my report, the hospital offered him a permanent place at the Day Centre twice a week where he would at least get a bath and a meal.

I was not there to witness the intervention by the Health Inspector, nor did I enquire too closely regarding the manner in which all was accomplished. Suffice to say that the house was cleared and some attempt made to clean it. The important thing was that George was as adequately catered for as possible and monitored regularly at the hospital. The saga of Main Road Farm could well have remained an almost forgotten incident among a host of others, had it not surfaced again three years later.

Just after this event took place I had qualified as a Practical Work Teacher, which meant that I was expected to train prospective district nurses and assess their competence to practice. The process required them to have a fortnight's induction first, which was considerably more than I ever received. Once this had been completed my entire caseload was handed over for them to manage, whilst they deployed the team, of which I became an ex-officio member. At the end of the day we would discuss the outcome and any problems, although I was never far away should they need me.

It isn't always an easy matter to stand back and watch another person assume your mantle and run your prized 'patch'. Nevertheless in the summer of 1978 I had no such qualms, as Nurse James was proving to be a capable and very compassionate student. So, when she arrived for the end of day briefing I was quite unprepared for her distress.

"Sister, I've honestly never seen anything like it," she wailed and launched into her account.

"Have you ever come across anyone called George Carpenter?" she asked.

"Goodness, that's a blast from the past," I said. "What's happened?"

"Well, Dr. Rivers said he'd had a letter from the hospital querying whether George was in fact taking all of his prescribed medication, and he asked me to visit and check. I called this afternoon and found the house to be rather dilapidated and the garden overgrown with a broken down fence and gate. I knocked on the back door and opened it to be confronted by a small, pale, emaciated, ill-looking female who simply stared at me."

"Ah, so you have actually met the elusive Hilda, which is more than I ever did."

"It was really weird. I asked her if I could talk to Mr. Carpenter and she simply grinned and went on tearing up newspaper into shreds, screwing it up and placing it either onto a table, a chair or into a bucket. The whole time I was there she spent doing this as if her life depended on it. But I never once heard her speak."

"Did you get to see George?"

"Yes, I found him in the dining room, sitting on the only available chair. He was very polite and answered all my questions, although he is very hard of hearing, which made it difficult at times. He's inclined to become breathless and is slightly cyanosed round the lips, but I checked and I'm quite sure that he is taking his tablets. He's clearly better nourished than his sister."

"So what's the problem?"

"Sister, the whole place is almost uninhabitable to what I would consider even the lowest standard of living. It looked as if nothing had ever been cleaned. Every shelf, table, chair and windowsill was full of clutter."

"Sounds familiar," I grinned. "I have very vivid memories of it."

"And there were insects and things crawling around and mouse droppings."

"Now, that is new. So, what do you propose to do?"

"Well, I went straight back to the surgery and told Dr. Rivers that I consider the place a health and safety risk and that I intend to report the whole matter to the appropriate authority."

"And what was his response?"

"That's just it. He's obviously truly concerned about the family, but is doubtful as to how much we should or could interfere. He maintains that they have a legal right to live as they desire, and if they're happy with things as they are, ought we to expect them to change anything?"

"And what do you think, Nurse?"

"Whilst I agree that everyone has a right to his or her own privacy, from a carer's point of view it's impossible," she almost cried.

"But has either of them asked for our intervention?"

"Well, no."

"And have they agreed to your offer of care?"

"No. George said they'd manage."

"Exactly, and therein is the dilemma. It is their home and we are merely guests. They don't have to accept us or our care. Added to which is Hilda actually a source of harm to others?"

"Probably not, but she's harming herself through negligence. She needs psychiatric care."

"Which won't happen unless Dr. Rivers seeks to have her sectioned, and I strongly suspect that he will shrink from that. Sleep on it, Nurse, and we'll beard him at the surgery in the morning. Meanwhile, I suggest you compile a report for the Community Nursing Officer voicing your concerns. In the event of the doctor not agreeing to act, we will then have covered our backs."

Reluctant as Dr. Rivers was to take any real action on the following day, he changed his mind a week later. When calling on the couple he was greeted by Hilda, shrieking like a banshee, telling him to, "Get the hell out of here!" accompanied by a fusillade of objects which happened to come to hand. Poor George was caught in the bombardment and the clearly demented Hilda was promptly admitted for psychiatric care, while George was placed in a residential home run by Social Services.

Shortly afterwards I happened to meet old Dr. Standish and related the story.

"I knew the whole family and I'm surprised those two siblings survived on their own at home for as long as they have. It's a pathetic tale but one which was not unfamiliar in days gone by. I have no intention of going into details, but I will simply say one word to you Sister: Incest!" He walked away.

Was Edward Carpenter's sexual appetite, his proclivity for breeding and the deaths of several other children, including a much older daughter, responsible for the unfortunate Hilda's state? Was Hilda in fact the result of a relationship between father and daughter? The hint imparted by the doctor highlighted yet another facet of community life which would never even have occurred to me. Acts such as incest were often not talked about outside the family and any unfortunate outcomes were accepted and passed off with a reasonable explanation. However, local gossip is inevitable and, more often than not, contains grains of truth. Memories are short and such goings-on tend to be forgotten, or simply subsumed into the folklore of a village.

None of us felt any satisfaction or pleasure at the outcome, which forced us to recognise that there are some situations in which we will never win.

Chapter Five. Some Hazards Of The Job

 Shortly after my arrival in Kent from the Midlands in 1969 I had my first taste of the local winter weather which can bring the area to a standstill. I also experienced the lengths to which some nurses will go to reach their patients, whilst others too readily use the weather as an excuse not to turn up.

I had just completed a hectic night duty in the maternity department of the hospital and was sitting in the office of one of the Senior Nursing Officers on the general wards, weighing up the snow which had been falling steadily all night and was now carpeting the landscape generously. It was a little after eight o'clock and I unenthusiastically contemplated the prospect of the drive home.

"Don't worry," she said, "I've driven in from the coast and it's quite manageable with care. The main roads are fine. Not," she added, "that it will stop some of our fainter-hearted colleagues from taking the opportunity to have a day off".

As though on cue, the phone rang and I listened with amusement to the one-sided conversation. In a firm cultured voice, that remained unendingly polite but with a steely undertone, I heard her say: "Oh dear, Nurse, I am sorry that you can't make it in. This weather's vile isn't it?" The person on the other end of the line clearly fervently agreed.

"Tell me, Nurse, exactly where do you live?" There was the briefest pause before her brisk response came. "What a coincidence. My home is quite close by and I got here without trouble. Even if you can't manage to get the car out of your road, you will find that the main roads are clear and the public transport system is working, both trains and buses. I'll expect you here within the hour, Nurse. Goodbye." The receiver was firmly replaced. "Nice try, but I'm afraid they'll have to get up earlier in order to put one across me," she smiled with satisfaction.

I managed to arrive home in one piece to the relief of concerned parents who clearly didn't have much faith in my ability to drive in these unaccustomed conditions. However, after a day's sleep I set out to return for duty only to learn that they were struggling to keep the main road open between our village and the coast. A helpful policeman assured me that with due care I should be able to reach the city in the other direction, but the snow was now falling ever more steadily and it was with grateful thanks that I reached my destination.

Mercifully, the entire night staff for the maternity unit had arrived except for one staff nurse who lived 14 miles away on the coast. Feeling sure that she would find the journey impossible I re-jigged the duties. With the mothers settled for the night and the corridor lights dimmed, I prepared to read some of the case notes. A movement beyond the office door caught my eye and looking up I was confronted by the figure of the errant Staff Nurse. Clad in the distinctive navy gabardine coat of the Queens Institute of District Nurses, a navy storm cap on her head with the flaps pulled down over her ears, a large muffler, gum boots and brown leather gauntlet gloves, she presented an amazing spectacle.

"Good heavens," I exclaimed, "I never thought you'd even attempt to come in. You look like Scott of the Antarctic."

"Never say die, Sister," she said in her broad Scottish accent. "I've known worse than this."

"Surely you didn't drive here?"

"No. I walked the two miles to the main road and managed to hitch a lift in the council gritting lorry which was following in the wake of a snowplough, but it was slow progress and jolly cold. My bladder reacted to every jolt," she said with feeling.

Fussed over by her colleagues and revived with hot tea she soon took herself off to commence her shift.

"And don't you worry, Sister, I'll definitely be here tomorrow night because I've bought my night clothes and toilet stuff and I'll kip down in the nurses home."

This was a woman nearing retirement and to me her attitude was an enduring example of loyalty, determination and commitment.

By the next morning most minor roads were impassable and still the snow came down. As it marked the beginning of my 'nights off' I was determined to make it home if possible. By following her example I too followed in the wake of the snowplough and managed to leave the car at the entrance to our lane and the long drive up to the house. My father emerged, intent on walking into the village to get milk and bread and whatever else was available, so I decided to accompany him.

Nothing could have prepared me for the sight that greeted us. Drawn up along the High Street was a veritable fleet of tractors whose drivers were all gathered in the chemist shop with the local Police Constable. Full of curiosity, we squeezed in behind in time to hear the pharmacist say: "Which of you is taking the prescriptions for the villages to the west?" Forward stepped a ruddy-faced farmer who lumbered out bearing two sizeable boxes, to add to the supply of bread and milk already in his trailer.

"Who is going to try and fetch the children stranded overnight at Swavely School?" queried the policeman. Off went another stalwart towing a truck with a pile of blankets underneath a tarpaulin.

The shop bell jangled and in came a figure strongly reminiscent of that presented by my Staff Nurse the previous night.

"Good morning Sister! Wrapped up nice and warm I hope? If you've got all your gear Tom's going to try and get you to your confinement."

"I'm afraid you'll have to perch in the pig trailer," said her would-be chauffeur. "I've put a bale of hay in there so you should be OK."

Giving my father a sharp nudge I whispered: "Nurse in a pig trailer! Remind me never to go on the district." Clearly I had forgotten this incident when I later did apply for the post, otherwise I would never have found myself in a similar position in the snow.

A New Year To Remember

The snow, which had flurried threateningly for a couple of days, began to fall in earnest on New Year's Eve. Relishing the thought of a week's annual leave ahead of me, I dashed round frantically trying to leave everything in order for my relief nurse. As the day progressed things were becoming ominous and, struggling to make my way home, I watched the snow blowing off the fields in fierce gusts, drifting in banks and reducing the main road to a single lane.

Thankfully parking the car in the garage, I unloaded my delivery equipment into the house, locked the door firmly and slipped into some comfortable gear. Clearly, our earlier plans to celebrate the occasion with friends was going to be a non-starter, confirmed by a phone call informing us that the road to their coastal town was now closed.

By midnight, my husband, in true acknowledgment of his Scottish roots, had made steady inroads into a bottle of whisky. We duly saw in the New Year and were preparing for bed when the strident ringing of the phone shattered the peace. It turned out to be a friend and former colleague who was a midwifery night sister at the hospital.

"I don't know whether you can help Ann," she said, "but we've got a bit of a problem. There's a mum expecting her first baby who's booked with us, but you probably know her because she comes from your neck of the woods. You've done some of her ante-natal care."

I did indeed recall the young farmer's wife who had also attended my relaxation classes.

"The thing is, she's gone into labour but her husband's scared to set out with her because of the snow and the ambulance men are having difficulty negotiating the hill out of the city. They've already got a vehicle stuck on another case and, to be frank, she sounds quite distressed. We wondered whether you could perhaps reach her as you're nearer?"

"Of course I'll have a go, although I don't know how successful I'll be. I'll keep you informed."

Replacing the receiver, I turned to face my incredulous husband.

"You must be out of your tiny mind! If the ambulance can't get through I don't know how you think you're going to."

"I've got to at least have a try."

"Well, there's no way that you're driving," he declared. "We'll go in my car as it's already out and facing the right direction."

With the equipment loaded on board, clad in anoraks and gum boots and armed with a couple of spades, we set out. The farm was only some three miles away, but it wasn't until 2 a.m. that we eventually arrived at the house, having dug ourselves out of drifts on three occasions and slithered perilously in a constant giddy waltz. I had the grace to admit that without the skill and efforts of my long-suffering spouse I would never have succeeded.

Lights shone out from various rooms and a relieved husband shepherded us inside. Jenny was lying on her bed alternately screaming and crying, but calmed down a little at my presence.

A swift examination revealed that the labour was well advanced and the cervix was some three inches dilated. However, to my horror the baby's head was firmly in a posterior position which didn't bode well, often requiring a forceps delivery. The first thing was to ease the discomfort of the contractions by administering an injection of Pethidine. Going downstairs I found the men drinking coffee, but my priority was the phone.

"Well, I've got to the house," I informed the Night Sister and I quickly outlined the scenario. "If I stay here with her and let things progress, what are my chances of a Flying Squad if things get stuck?"

"Pretty slim," came the reply, "although the ambulance station has rung to say that they've fitted a set of chains to the vehicle and are currently attempting to get to you."

"In that case, I'll put Jenny in my car and we'll set out from this end and hopefully we'll meet up somewhere en route. Perhaps you'd let them know? If the worst happens we can always stop off at my house which we can hopefully reach again."

Although he didn't say anything, I knew my husband was viewing this foray with grave misgivings, especially as the patient, now wrapped in dressing gown and blanket, appeared clutching a bowl and announcing that she felt sick.

"Not nearly as sick as I feel," said my husband in an undertone. "She's not going to have this baby in my car, is she?"

"Very unlikely, unless you manage to turn it upside-down," I responded somewhat tartly.

Collecting her things she followed us out of the house, locking the door behind her, and we settled her on the back seat. Jenny demanded to know the whereabouts of her husband and was reassured to find that he had gone to the barn to get his tractor and a rope so that he could tow us out if necessary. So we set off, with Jenny labouring noisily whilst I tried to encourage her to summon up the techniques practiced at the relaxation classes.

Mercifully it had stopped snowing and an eerie quiet surrounded us save for the sound of the engine and crunch of the car tyres as they negotiated the terrain.

It was with profound relief that, as we reached our home at 3.45 a.m., we saw the blue light of an ambulance coming towards us. Gratefully we transferred the patient and I prepared to climb in with her.

"Who are you?" the ambulance man queried.

I grinned. "Despite this unlikely garb, I'm the midwife, would you believe? I'm afraid I'll have to accompany her as I've administered Pethidine."

"That's fine, Sister, but how are you going to get back?"

Eying my husband somewhat tentatively I replied: "Well, hopefully he'll follow in your tracks." Rob's expression was not sunny!

By 4.45 a.m. we arrived at the hospital and handed over our charge. Declining the offer to stay and deliver the baby, we set out to retrace our steps. As we prepared to tackle the hill we saw, trundling towards us, the unmistakable shape of a tractor.

"You took your time," we called through the window.

"My stupid wife locked the door behind her and has obviously got the key with her," he responded gloomily

"Well, cheer up, she's doing fine. A Happy New Year to you," we chorused.

"Some New Year this has been," remarked my husband. "You do realise that if the police had stopped me I'd have been way over the limit, don't you?"

Somehow, I didn't think there would have been too many patrol cars out that night.

Little Amy turned out to be the first baby of the New Year and a report of our exploits made headline news in the local paper. Over the years I watched her grow and thought to myself: "You little know the palaver your arrival caused."

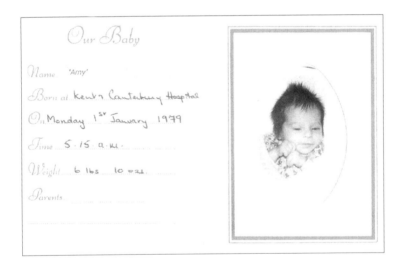

Our Baby

Name 'Amy'

Born at Kent & Canterbury Hospital

On Monday 1st January 1979

Time 5.15 a.m.

Weight 6 lbs 10 ozs.

Parents

108

Build Me An Ark

The summer of 1976 had been particularly hot and sunny and the harvest was well advanced. It was the kind of weather that made you grateful to have a job which took you out of doors and I felt something akin to relief when the rain actually began to fall in mid-September. At last we could breathe. Throughout the night I was half-conscious of the continual, steady sound of driving rain as it beat a tattoo on the window.

I was brought fully to life by the ringing of the phone.

"Good morning Sister," said a cheerful man's voice. "We've waited as long as possible before calling you, but the wife's gone into labour and I think it would be a good idea if you made your way in this direction."

Mrs. Lake was a sensible woman. She and her farmer husband already had three strong young lads and they ran a very successful outfit.

"I'll be there straight away," I responded.

"Be a bit careful how you go Sister, because the lanes are beginning to run with water." Well, a little water would be a welcome change, or so I thought.

Slipping a raincoat over my uniform dress I got the car out of the garage and set off. The main road presented no problem and I splashed gaily on my way. By the time I reached the village in which the surgery was situated I became aware of water running liberally down the side streets. Standing on the corner by the chemist shop I spotted two of the doctors, both sporting gum boots, and pulled up beside them.

"Where are you off to Sister?"

"Mrs. Lake down at Hollow Farm has gone into labour."

"Mind how you go then because things are getting a bit iffy. The fields are baked dry and can't absorb the volume of rain that's fallen, so the lanes are becoming like rivers. According to reports, we're experiencing flash flooding."

I glanced at the swirling muddy stream but still didn't think too much of it and headed off in the direction of the farm. Leaving the village behind, the road gave way to a lane with fields on either side bounded by high banks down which were pouring streams of filthy water, which was turning the lane into a river. As it swirled menacingly round the car I urged my little Morris Minor on, praying that it wouldn't stall. For a few more yards all was well but, just as the farm came into sight in the distance, half a mile away in a dip, so the car gave up the ghost. To my horror I saw water seeping in and I vainly tried to follow the telephone lines in the hope of spotting a house nearby, but no such luck.

There had been nothing in my training which prepared the midwife for such an event but one thing was for sure, I couldn't just sit there. The water filled my shoes as I collected my bags from the boot and concentrated my mind on the best way to try to get to the farm. It was so frustrating to be able to see it, so near and yet so far.

Then I spotted something moving and watched as a tractor navigated its way slowly towards me through the swirling waters.

"I was watching out for you Sister and spotted your car from the bedroom window. Give me your things and then climb up behind me," said my rescuer.

By now I was thoroughly soaked.

"Is your wife alright?" I queried anxiously.

"I reckon she'll hang on until you get there."

With gratitude I tumbled into the sanctuary of the immaculate farm kitchen where I proceeded to drip liberally over the floor. The patient's mother took one look at me and suggested that I strip off while she tried to find me something else to put on. Thus it was that clad in a dressing gown and slippers I introduced another lusty boy into a water-logged world. Having witnessed the happy event the baby's father prepared to leave.

"I've sent two of my chaps to try and retrieve your car," he said. "Actually, if you come across to the window you'll see they're bringing it in now."

There, on the end of a tow rope, was my precious vehicle looking decidedly the worse for wear.

"Don't worry Sister, we'll pop it in the drying shed and tinker around a bit and by the time you're ready to go all should be well – fingers crossed."

"And your clothes are drying on the Aga," said Granny, "so just get this cup of coffee down you and relax."

I offered up a fervent prayer of thanks that this escapade had occurred whilst caring for this wonderful family.

It was almost lunchtime when I finally left the farm, after a morning that had seemed to last forever. True to his word my car appeared, cleaned and functional once more.

"You're getting a bit low on petrol Sister and I'm afraid I can't help you there - we've only got diesel."

"Oh, I'll get some in the village, no problem."

Only, as it turned out, there was. Having escorted me and the car as far as the High Street the farm hand returned to the farm and I drove onto the garage forecourt.

"Sorry Sister, the water's flooded the tanks, added to which we've got no power. But don't worry, they're OK three miles up the road, I've just checked."

Driving past the pharmacy I decided to stop to collect some prescriptions I had ordered, in time to meet the chemist's wife emerging, clutching an armful of packets of sanitary towels.

"Vee are not open zis morning, Sister, and I do not fink vee shall be open zis afternoon," she trilled in her heavy European accent. "All zee cellars are flooded and everything it floats. I am rescuing, yes."

Having eventually successfully refuelled the car and changed into boots, I tried to work out which of my routine patients I would safely be able to reach. Consulting with the surgery, I learned that between the team all but the most remote had been catered for. However, Mrs. Marks, who had been on my list, still remained. Well into her eighties, she lived alone in a somewhat dilapidated tied cottage, where she and her husband had been allowed to stay following his retirement. For a peppercorn rent they had a roof over their heads but, as in so many similar cases, little if anything was done to maintain or improve such properties. In truth, the landlord was often praying that they would move, so that a realistic rent could be charged once the property had been modernised. Some would yield even better profit if sold for development.

Mrs. Marks wasn't the easiest or most endearing of people. Now widowed and with deteriorating sight and mobility, she also had congestive cardiac failure and the ubiquitous leg ulcer.

Initial tempts to reach her failed, as I was twice turned back by the fire brigade busily trying to pump out roads and houses. Following their instructions I took a circuitous route to reach my destination. Parking the car in the lane I set out to pick a path through the garden which was completely flooded, and promptly lost one of my wellingtons.

Eventually I reached the wooden front door, knocked and pushed it open. It gave way onto the most pathetic scene. The whole of the downstairs was under two inches of water. Sitting huddled at the top of the stairs in a state of abject despair was Mrs. Marks. Upon seeing me she reverted to her usual ascerbic tone,

"Do you know Sister, nobody's been near me," she said in an aggrieved voice. "I haven't seen a soul all day."

Gently I tried to describe the situation which prevailed but she clearly wasn't impressed.

"I've had nothing to eat or drink and I can't get to the kitchen because of the water. Goodness knows what all this has done to my carpet."

I smiled wryly, for Mrs. Mark's carpet was threadbare to the point of any pattern being completely unrecognisable, and I would hazard that it hadn't been cleaned for years.

"Look, first of all I'll come upstairs and we'll get the dressing on your leg done. I will then see what I can find in the kitchen to feed you on."

I was just finishing bandaging her leg when a knock came at the door and a male voice called out, "Mrs. Marks are you alright?" It was her landlord who pulled a face at the sodden floor, but promptly asked what he could do to help.

"The most pressing need is for her to be fed and watered," I said.

Before I could continue a voice came sharply from upstairs: "You're not getting me out of here, I'm staying put."

"Mrs. Marks," I replied, "nobody is moving you, but we have got to do what we can to make sure that you are not at risk of harm."

Once more salvation came, this time in the shape of the landlord.

"I suggest that nurse helps you to get things comfortable up there. Meanwhile, I'll go home and get my wife to prepare a meal for you. I will then bring it back along with a couple of thermos flasks of tea. That should see you OK until morning when we'll review the situation."

The recipient of this generous offer reluctantly had the grace to agree that it was very kind.

Going to the door with him I thanked him profusely.

"Honestly Sister, it's not that I want her out but she really shouldn't be here in her state."

"I totally agree and after this little episode, if I have anything to do with it, every effort will be made to rehouse her. There are two old peoples' bungalows coming up shortly in the village, so I'll see what can be done."

Sure enough, following prompt liaison with the local housing department and the appropriate doctor's letter, a speedy response was effected. With added pressure from an only son, who lived in the city, and would be only too pleased of anything that absolved him from feeling that he ought to be doing something, a grumbling Mrs. Marks was rehoused, even before Christmas had arrived.

Alarming and disrupting as the flash floods had been, at least there was one satisfactory outcome, although it took many, many months before a certain lady would reluctantly admit it.

The Great Storm

The great storm of October 1987 made a considerable impression on many people, never more so than in the south-east corner of England. Nobody could recall anything like it. That evening dusk had come quickly and although it remained very windy, the heavy rain had stopped. The weathermen had merely warned of severe gusts, so we retired to bed unconcerned and slept soundly, blissfully unaware of the drama unfolding outside.

At about five in the morning I roused from an uninterrupted sleep to find my husband hurriedly pulling on some clothes and muttering that 'something odd' was going on.

"You stay there," he said. "There's quite a gale blowing outside and I've just heard an almighty crash, so I'll just go and investigate."

To add emphasis to his words an object landed on the ground beneath the bedroom window. Minutes later he was back.

"There seems to be one hell of a storm and that noise was our garage roof which has been taken off by the wind. The crash I heard was part of it hurling itself into our neighbour's bedroom window, and what was left has landed on your car and caved the freezer lid in. There are also a number of tiles off the roof and part of the chimney."

The abrupt delivery of such news does tend to have the effect of electrifying mind and body into action.

"Are the Bates OK?" I asked as I struggled into a track suit.

"Fortunately their daughter was so upset that they'd moved into her bedroom at the back of the house, shortly before it happened."

As we opened the front door, the eerie sound of creaking and groaning assaulted our ears and we saw the ancient beech tree opposite slowly spread its majestic length across the main road and our drive. Then we spotted the broken roof tiles and were in time to hear the unmistakable sound of splintering glass, as the greenhouse became a twisted skeleton of metal framework. This was possibly the storm's last fling, after which a strange quietness enveloped us. Gradually the severity of the situation became apparent. The power lines were down but the telephone was still operational. I gave thanks for a coal-fired Raeburn which ensured some warmth and the means to supply hot food and drinks. It soon became clear that many in the vicinity were less fortunate. Rob set up a hurricane lamp and, after ringing round the family to check on them, I set about devising a plan of action.

"There is no way you'll be able to get any nursing visits done," Rob said. "Not only can you not get out until that tree has been removed, but the windscreen of your car is completely shattered."

Clearing the road after the 1987 storm

The team of nurses covering our extensive rural area lived in various different locations and this helped considerably. Most, like me, were unable to pursue the normal routine of calls as the extent of roads blocked by fallen trees became clear. The decision was taken to allocate the work geographically which meant that, between us, a proportion of the visits could be done on foot. It wasn't a prospect that any of us exactly relished but, 'needs must when the devil drives' and he was certainly digging the spurs in that morning.

Evidence of a true Dunkirk spirit emerged as younger members of the community checked on the elderly and vulnerable. Most of the patients I visited were frankly amazed by my arrival. Cries of: "Sister, you shouldn't have bothered. We'd manage somehow," invariably greeted us.

Not so from old Stanley Noyes. Living in a fairly isolated cottage along a narrow lane, I negotiated the fallen debris and finally arrived at his back door to find him relaxing in an armchair by the Raeburn drinking a cup of tea.

"Well done, Sister. You've made it - the paper boy hasn't."

"Thank you," I replied, somewhat sarcastically. "It's so nice to know that I rank just above the paper boy in your estimation."

"I'll have you know I look forward to my newspaper each day. It's routine, but the youngsters haven't got any staying power these days."

"Mr. Noyes," I said, "have you listened to the news on the radio this morning?"

"Yes. Heard there'd been a bit of a storm or som'at," he remarked casually.

"That is an understatement, to say the least. Has it not dawned on you that due to blocked roads and railway lines, the papers haven't even made it to the newsagents?"

"Well, it never happened during the war," he declared stubbornly. "No matter what Hitler threw at us we always had our newspapers. It's like I said, nobody's got any backbone or stamina."

Arriving home to grab something for lunch, I found that my husband, armed with a chain saw and assisted by three neighbours, had made good progress in clearing the main road and our own access to it. The priority now was to try and ensure that I had a set of wheels. The nearest workshop where I could replace my windscreen proved to be an outfit situated on the outskirts of the city. A phone call elicited the information that there was already a queue of vehicles stretching for quite a distance, all intent on the same thing.

"Quite frankly," said the voice, "there isn't much point coming in today because I don't think we'll even clear this lot." Obviously it was time to plead my case.

"Oh! That's a different matter, Sister. We're operating a separate queue for essential services. Just come in as soon as you can."

My earlier perambulation round the village and its immediate environs had in no way prepared me for the incredible sights which now met me at every turn of the road, as I made detour after detour to get into the city. Rows of massive trees lay tossed down like skittles, with their root boles sticking out of the ground. Others had been snapped off like matchsticks and reduced to skeletons. Roofs were sprouting tarpaulins or plastic sheeting and 'road closed' signs proliferated.

Some rather glaring faces greeted me as I overtook the long line of cars awaiting attention at the workshop, although once they had spied the uniform the reaction changed. Immediately in front of me was a doctor I recognised from the hospital and we exchanged experiences.

"Honest to God, Sister, there I was driving cautiously down the motorway when I found myself being overtaken by a garden shed!"

Our conversation came to an abrupt halt as we gazed in astonishment at the car just arriving. Sticking out of the passenger side of the windscreen was the sawn-off remains of a fir tree which had neatly speared it.

The mechanic who came to deal with my problem took one look and said: "Blimey Sister, it looks as if you've been hit by shrapnel." As it transpired, there was hardly a part of the car which didn't require the attentions of a panel beater and the subsequent complete re-spray. That, however, was for another day. The garage roof had indeed left its mark.

Despite everything, by the following day the rural nursing team was more or less functioning as usual although we were hampered by the lack of power, which took three to five days to restore, and the odd broken telephone wire which prevented communications for one or two of us.

The local landscape had changed forever and the tower and spire of the listed village church took considerable time and money to renew. It was certainly a night to live in the memory.

Things Mechanical

The weather was not the only hazard with which the District Nurse had to contend. Totally reliant on the motor car, anything which affected the smooth running of our vehicles could throw the day into turmoil.

The working of the internal combustion engine was of absolutely no interest to me at all. My only concern was having a chassis on four wheels that would get me from A to B. Filling it with petrol, and checking the oil and water constituted the limit of my expertise. On the mercifully infrequent occasions when I sustained a puncture there had always been a willing farmer, patient's husband or my long-suffering father prepared to sort things out. However, when I remarried, Rob decided that I ought to learn to change a wheel. I spent a morning trying to take in the instructions without any great enthusiasm, and then promptly forgot about it.

Only a few weeks later on a Saturday morning, literally in the middle of nowhere, the rear off-side tyre suffered a puncture. Recognising that the likelihood of a knight in shining armour appearing along the lane was very remote, I was forced to put my newly learnt skills to the test.

Cursing loudly, I set about unloading the contents of the boot, found the jack and humped the spare wheel out. To my considerable surprise all went smoothly and, by the time I slid back behind the wheel, I was feeling extremely proud of myself. Dropping the punctured tyre off at the local garage, I headed home, eager to phone my husband, who was away on business in Cheshire, and boast of my prowess.

"H'mm! Are you sure you completely tightened all the nuts?"

"Of course I did," I replied, "I'm not stupid."

"Even so, I'd feel much happier if you got the chaps to check when you collect the wheel."

Arriving at the garage I made my request and set off on foot to visit a nearby patient. Upon my return I was greeted by three mechanics with huge grins on their faces, who immediately broke into a rendition of Burt Baccarach's 'Three Wheels on my Wagon'.

"What's going on?" I demanded.

"It's not so much what's going on, but what's coming off," the foreman replied.

"There are only two ways to screw a nut on, Sister. You've managed to get every one of them back-to-front with the result that they were all steadily working themselves loose. Your husband was right to be suspicious."

Considerably chastened, I offered my thanks.

"In future Sister, just stick to the human body and leave all things mechanical to us."

This was something that I was more than willing to do and I have never attempted to change a wheel again.

Motoring Accidents

I suppose it was more or less inevitable that at some point during 18 years on the district I would be involved in a road accident. Approaching a sharp left-hand bend on a country lane one day, I made abrupt, head-on contact with a vehicle being driven by an elderly gentleman on the wrong side of the road. The apologetic explanation offered by my unharmed assailant, that he was intent on not running over a dog sunbathing peacefully in his path, did not exactly impress me. Not only did my car protest strongly but my body was also none too happy.

The insurance company, keen to extract damages from my adversary, referred me to a Harley Street consultant in order to have the likelihood of any future problems which may result from my minimal injuries properly assessed. As far as I was concerned severe whiplash, and a multi-coloured, swollen knee, didn't constitute much of a threat.

Entering through the portal of a house on the famously hallowed street I was ushered into the gracious office of an immaculately suited, dignified but unsmiling orthopaedic surgeon. Complying with the instructions to strip to my bra and pants and lie down on the couch, I was then submitted to the equivalent of an MOT test. Gravely, every portion of my anatomy was examined and reflexes tested. I obligingly struggled to sit up without using my arms and dutifully raised each leg in turn while attempting to keep them perfectly straight. This was not as simple as it sounds, due to the fact that I had a history of previously prolapsed intravertebral discs.

Eventually, once more fully dressed, I sat in front of the imposing desk to await the verdict.

"I understand you are a nurse," he said.

Having confirmed the correctness of this statement, my examiner solemnly continued: "Although I see no immediate problem resulting from your accident, I am going to give you some free advice."

"And that is?" I asked innocently.

"Give up nursing," came the unexpected reply.

"I beg your pardon," I managed to gasp.

"With the back you've got, you are in the wrong profession."

"How have you reached that conclusion?" I demanded.

Clearly unused to having his judgment questioned, he eyed me coolly before remarking disinterestedly: "You have barely a 60 degree lift in your left leg and only 45 degrees in your right."

Such a profound statement obviously needed a response.

"Do you know," I replied, "I'm not in the habit of trying to nurse my patients lying flat on my back with my legs in the air."

It soon became apparent that this illustrious personage was completely lacking in even a vestige of humour, and I was politely but promptly escorted to the door. The consultation was over.

In all fairness he was probably right, but 'bad backs' were simply considered an inconvenient and painful occupational hazard at the time. Undoubtedly they accounted for many days of sick leave amongst the staff. Meanwhile, manual handling training programmes and mechanical hoists were only just coming into being.

All God's Creatures

Very early on I came to realise that for the nurse working in a rural practice a love of livestock great and small is desirable, along with the ability to handle them. The maxim 'love me love my dog' was often all too true. However, I soon found that some creatures are infinitely more acceptable than others which can, in fact, present a considerable hazard.

Joe Taylor and his wife were the caretakers of a rather impressive Georgian-style mansion which was scheduled to be sold for redevelopment as a hotel if all the plans went through. Whilst Renie's domain was the house itself, Joe was responsible for the extensive grounds.

I first met them when I was called to re-dress the mangled toes on one of his feet following an argument with a rather powerful lawnmower. It was clear from the start that the way to his heart was via a lively terrier dog which was never far from his side. Despite his injuries Joe still managed to keep going and I never knew which part of the gardens I would have to drag him from in order to carry out my task.

On the day of my last visit he was attempting to clear a large ornamental lily pond and, as I appeared, he indicated a bucket and fishing net beside him.

"I thought your girls would like to have these, Sister," he said.

Peering in I saw three goldfish swimming round in their plastic prison and my heart dipped a few inches. The last of the fish that had accompanied us from the Midlands had only recently expired and I hadn't planned to replace them. "That's really kind of you," I smiled. "They will be well pleased."

With the dressing removed and the toes pronounced healed, I drove slowly home with the bucket and its occupants sloshing about on the floor of the car between my legs.

It was seven years before I met up with Joe again, by which time the goldfish had long since departed to swim in the sky. The grand house was now under new ownership and the couple had been allocated an old people's council bungalow with a large garden in a village some 10 or so miles away. However, there would be no more gardening for Joe as he lay in bed, his once active body now merely a shell that housed a heart which was fast losing the will to live. He had been discharged from hospital and come home to die – another victim of lung cancer. Curled up beside him was a much older terrier, also showing signs of age. If he remembered me he gave no sign.

I put on a nursing gown and prepared to wash and shave the patient, but when I tried to oust the dog from his comfortable spot on the blankets, I was met with a rumbling growl and the curl of the mouth. Calling to Renie I explained the predicament.

"Come here you stupid animal and let Sister get on. She's not going to hurt Joe."

Clearly this statement was in dispute as he continued to voice his displeasure. By dint of tugging and brute force, though, Alfie was finally persuaded into the living room.

This exercise continued on a daily basis for almost a fortnight. Joe was on regular morphine injections and each time I visited he had deteriorated further. Neither Renie nor anyone else would have wished for him to linger. The main thing was that he was comfortable, pain-free and peaceful.

I had visited early on a Saturday morning and discovered him to be totally unresponsive, so I was not surprised when the phone rang at lunchtime and to hear Renie saying: "Can you come, Sister, I think he's gone."

Driving straight over, one quick examination proved her right.

The Taylors had no children, but she did have a brother living in Wiltshire who she had already phoned and he was preparing to drive across and give her what help he could.

"What have I got to do now, Sister?" she asked helplessly.

I sat with her and gently explained the need to contact an undertaker.

"But I don't know any," she wailed.

The District Nurses were used to being consulted on such matters and I suggested a local firm with whom I had built a good relationship. The director was a true professional, had the most wonderful, gentle manner and was always prepared to go the extra mile, especially for the elderly and those without family support.

I set about the task of performing the last offices, not helped by the ever-present Alfie who refused, point blank, to get off the bed. He barely tolerated my ministrations, growling and turning his head at each movement, but I decided he had a right to stay by the side of his master for one last time. As I was finishing, the undertaker arrived with one of his team of bearers and talked with Renie in the lounge.

"All finished, Sister?"

"Well, I've done the best I can." Turning to the wife I suggested that she might like to come and spend a moment with Joe.

When she returned I indicated that I would sit with her while they removed Joe's body. The trouble was I'd forgotten about Alfie! Suddenly there was a positive eruption of snarling, growling and barking and two shaken-looking men hastily retreated back into the lounge. "Sister, do you think you could take charge of the dog and preferably shut him in another room?"

"Renie, I know this is hard but I'm afraid he won't let any of us move him," I said.

Returning to the bedside she prepared to grab Alfie's collar for the usual tugging performance. Neither of us were ready for the response though, as he sunk his teeth into her arm. Mercifully she had a very substantial heavy jacket on but, even so, the animal managed to leave a faint imprint. We all retreated to the lounge.

"I'm afraid he's always been Joe's dog," Renie explained. "I've never been that bothered about animals, but those two were inseparable."

"Any suggestions, Sister?" asked the undertaker.

"Well, I'm certainly not going into the arena with the lions. If you can't manage there's only one solution and that's the vet."

"Perhaps you could entice him into the kitchen with some food, Mrs. Taylor?" the undertaker suggested, without much conviction. In the event his doubts were justified. Alfie was having none of that.

In the end it was the young bearer who bravely solved the situation.

"Get his lead," he said. "I'm going to pin him down on the bed with this short carpet runner. If he tries to bite he won't do any harm. While I hold his head and muzzle down, you attach the lead to his collar."

I don't think Alfie knew quite what had hit him but it was distressing, nevertheless. With his muzzle well and truly pinioned under the rug, all was safely accomplished. The angry and thoroughly agitated terrier was pulled into the kitchen and the door firmly closed. Speedily Joe's body was removed and the relieved undertaker made his escape while, all the while, Alfie continued to make his displeasure felt.

"What's going to happen when you let him out?" I asked Renie apprehensively.

"I've absolutely no idea, Sister, I really haven't. He's never, ever gone for me before."

"Well, I certainly can't leave you to do it on your own," I said. "How long will it be until your brother arrives?"

"I don't know I'm sure," she said wearily.

Suddenly, it dawned on me that while we had been talking everything had gone quiet. With considerable trepidation I opened the kitchen door a crack, then a bit further. Giving it a final push I stood back. Out trotted Alfie, who walked sedately past both of us and into the bedroom. We waited but all was peaceful.

"He's probably gone to curl up on the bed again," said Renie.

Scarcely were the words out of her mouth when the little chap reappeared. Completely ignoring both of us, he went straight to Joe's chair jumped up on it and settled down to sleep.

"Thank goodness," I breathed, and we both relaxed.

"I don't know Sister. What do you make of that?"

"I can only assume that he realises what has happened and is now prepared to accept the inevitable," I guessed. The ways of humans are often peculiar and animals are no different.

An Unusual Pedicure

It wasn't long after Joe's death that I came to the conclusion that a District Nurse's training should include a veterinary module. One afternoon the receptionist greeted me with her usual smile and asked me if I'd got a moment.

"I've had a phone call from old Mrs. Baker in the High Street. It was a bit difficult to get a coherent message, because she's well into her eighties and being virtually stone deaf she shouts. All I could gather is that she wants the nurse to come and see to her toe nails."

"I'm not a chiropodist," I moaned.

"You try and explain that to her over the phone," Jane grimaced.

"Oh alright, I'll go and see what I can do."

"I'd better warn you that she can sometimes be a bit... " She hesitated.

"A bit what?" I asked suspiciously.

"Well, the police were called not so long ago because there had been complaints from the neighbours that she was emptying her chamber pot out of her bedroom window in the mornings. Her toilet is downstairs and she either can't or won't be bothered to bring it down," she smiled apologetically.

"Great," I exclaimed. "All I need is a barmy old girl who's decided to go mediaeval on us."

Guessing that she wouldn't hear my knock, I went in by the back door, then through the kitchen and dining room to the front room.

"Hello nurse," she almost cackled. "They gave you my message then?"

"Yes. I hear you've got some problems with your feet," I replied, trying to enunciate slowly and clearly.

"No dear, my teeth are alright."

I drew in a deep breath and tried again.

"I understand you are having difficulty with your toe nails?"

Staring at me in obvious puzzlement she replied, "No, I've never been to Wales dear."

Deciding that action would be better than speech, I opened my nursing case and took out the pair of nail clippers with which we were all issued. Turning back I showed them to her and indicated that I wanted to remove her slippers. Preparing to kneel on the floor I was nearly deafened by her guffaw of laughter. Patting me on the shoulder she said, "No dear, not mine, it's Billy's," and she indicated a cage in the corner. Therein reposed a multicoloured parrot of, what seemed to me, fairly generous proportions and who was casting a beady eye in my direction. Equally substantial claws were wrapped around a perch.

Standing up I looked at her and shook my head. Placing my mouth close to her ear, I all but shouted, "You need the vet."

She certainly heard that alright as back came the response, "Not on your life. He'll charge."

123

Suddenly the National Health Service assumed a whole new aspect. I had no intention whatsoever of even attempting this procedure. Not only did I possess a dislike of all things feathered that had tendencies to flutter alarmingly, I wouldn't even know where to start. Replacing the clippers I took out a piece of notepaper and printed on it, *'I will go and have a word with the vet and see if his nurse will come.'*

Mrs. Baker looked none too impressed but I resolutely gathered my things and bid that lady goodbye.

Fortunately, the practice had very friendly relations with the local vet. One explanatory phone call was all it took for them to agree to visit and sort the problem out free of charge. This was yet another example of community spirit.

The Butt Of The Matter

A communication came from the Maternity Department at the hospital requesting the midwife to visit Denise Mount at Lime Kiln Cottage, Stonebridge. She had been discharged following a caesarean section and required removal of remaining sutures and post-natal care. I had never met anyone of this name at the ante-natal clinic so was a little puzzled. As the doctors were gathered for their morning coffee I decided to make some enquiries.

"They're newcomers and have only just moved here," said Dr. Standish. "The husband is employed on one of the farms and this is their first baby."

"That accounts for the reason she isn't known to me," I said.

"When are you visiting?" the doctor asked.

"Probably this afternoon."

"May I just offer a word of warning?" he smiled.

"Please do."

"I called there yesterday thinking she would already be home but got no reply. However, I did come up against a large black dog which is none too friendly. There was a sign on the gate to that effect," he added ruefully.

"Did it go for you?" I asked apprehensively.

"Fortunately it was on the end of a long tether tied to an apple tree in the middle of the front garden. Don't go charging in and keep well to the hedge as you work your way round the perimeter."

Sure enough, as I pulled the car up in the lane and got out, I could both see and hear the hound in question dancing in a frenzy on the end of the leash. Gripping my nursing case firmly I cautiously opened the gate and inched in, not taking my eye off the creature. Trying to work out just how far the rope would allow him to go wasn't easy but, keeping close to the hedge line I made my way towards the back door. All was just as Dr. Standish had described. Then suddenly I was propelled forward and almost lost my footing as something hit me in the rear. He had completely omitted to mention the attendant billy goat.

While frantically trying to regain my balance, I heard a voice calling out. "Are you alright?" Standing by the back door was Denise with the baby in her arms.

"Let's just say that I'm shaken, well and truly stirred, but not quite grounded," I replied.

"You needn't worry because there's no way the dog could actually get at you," she said reassuringly.

"It's not the dog that's the problem. I was warned about him, but there was no mention of a goat," I sighed.

She laughed apologetically. "He won't hurt you but the truth is that he doesn't really like women."

Making a mental note to come dressed in a suit of armour on any future visits I went inside to tackle the remaining sutures.

Avian Defenders and Missing Cats

Doctor Rivers was the person responsible for sending me off on a goose chase one fine spring morning, except that on this occasion I wasn't the one doing the chasing.

"See what you can do for Bert Hodges, Sister. He's got chronic oedema of both legs and his wife is fighting a losing battle with them." I groaned inwardly, for I was rapidly coming to the conclusion that I had the most leg ulcer prone practice in Kent, not to mention the most constipated, judging by the number of enemas the nurses were requested to administer. No one would have thought that we were literally surrounded by fruit trees!

For nurses in the community, treating patients with leg ulcers was, and still is, all too common. In my early years on the district there were no compression bandages, and no clinical nurse specialists in wound care, so it was up to each district nurse to do the best she could with minimal tools.

Cellulitis and lower limb oedema can also result in ulceration and poor quality of life for the patients. As the limb becomes filled with fluid it also becomes increasingly immobile and so does the whole patient. The skin appears thickened and breaks down with lymph exuding through it, often in copious amounts, leading to ulceration.

Obesity is often another factor which, in turn, renders the recommended treatment almost impossible. Patients are advised to lose weight and exercise as much as possible, but most of them are incapable of walking more than a short distance and then require the support of sticks or a zimmer frame. Similarly they have to be encouraged to attempt small regular movements like fidgeting and bending the ankle backward and forward to aid the lymphatic return.

Treatment to reduce exudates is by means of leg elevation, preferably periods of lying down with the limb higher than the heart, all of which is unacceptable and virtually impossible for most elderly patients living at home, who already struggle to get themselves in and out of bed.

Bert Hodges proved to be a prime example. He and his wife lived in a newish bungalow, which they had built on a piece of land once part of a small farm and orchard owned by them but long since sold. Mrs. Hodges was a quiet, neat woman in her late seventies, fairly tall, slim and always on the go. There was nothing in the hamlet except a run-down pub and only two buses a week conveyed the residents to the town some five miles distant. This she visited on both occasions for the purposes of shopping, coffee and a chat with friends at the Retirement Centre.

Bert was the complete antithesis. Seemingly devoid of any conversation, and grossly overweight, he spent all day in the kitchen wedged into a carver chair, strongly reminiscent of a figure of Buddha but much less gilded. His oedematous legs stuck out in front of him like two tree trunks, while a pint tumbler of water occupied the table to one side. Resting on a chair to his right a white enamel urinal stood sentinel. The flies of his trousers remained permanently undone, gaping wide across his pendulous abdomen, in order to respond to the urgency with which he needed to frequently urinate, as a result of his diuretic medication. Both legs were heavily padded and bandaged in order to accommodate the continuous seepage of fluid. It was not a pretty sight!

However, before the unfortunate nurse could commence her ministrations there was a hurdle to overcome. Mr. and Mrs. Hodges were the owners of four very large white geese, who were of an age where they would have made pretty tough eating. These creatures roamed freely outside the premises and in the orchard. Sometimes they would be hidden out of sight but, more often than not, the moment a car drew up for instance, they appeared, ready to charge the driver the minute he or she emerged.

Once the sanctuary of the bungalow was gained the visitor was then faced with a veritable collection of cats which prowled the kitchen or draped themselves on the furniture, window sill or any convenient surface. One of these feline friends had developed a predilection for Bert's crepe bandages which his patient wife washed, dried and rolled after each nursing visit and placed in a cardboard box. Having suggested that it wasn't really in the best interests of hygiene to apply these to his legs after the cat had been happily nestling amongst them, Mrs. Hodges placed them like soldiers in the pigeon holes of an ancient bureau, which stood in one corner, and closed the flap.

Arriving one morning, my heart sank as I saw the four geese waddling perilously close to the back door, seemingly innocently engaged in foraging. Gripping my nursing case firmly in my right hand, I exited the car as stealthily as possible. Scarcely had I taken one step than this feathered squadron went into action. With heads down, much loud hissing and orange beaks all too evident they charged. Wildly swinging the case round and giving a not implausible impression of a whirling dervish, I careered at speed towards the back door where a wooden ramp was in place to accommodate Bert's wheelchair. With one flying leap I landed fair and squarely on the ramp only for my feet to disappear straight through it, as the creaking boards collapsed beneath me. The door flew open and Mrs. Hodges calmly dispatched the offending geese whilst I attempted to extricate my ruined nylons and grazed ankles.

Once safely inside I tried to recover my poise.

"Oh dear," she said, "you are in a state Sister. They'd never hurt you, you know."

"I prefer not to put it to the test," I assured her fervently. "I can now see why geese so effectively defended Rome."

"Did they really, dear? Well I never knew that," she beamed.

Meanwhile, Bert had sat completely unperturbed by the upheaval, as though such things were an everyday occurrence. Turning towards him, his wife quite calmly informed him: "I've been telling you for ages that the ramp was rotten. Well, thank goodness it was Sister who went through it and not you in your wheelchair!"

I suppose she had a point, although I was trying very hard to appreciate it.

"Honestly Sister, this is becoming quite a day. We've already had a bit of sadness."

"Oh dear," I exclaimed. "Whatever's happened?"

For once, the normally silent Bert gave voice.

"Blossom's disappeared," he mumbled morosely.

The female in question was one of the five resident cats, although I would have been incapable of identifying which one. Clearly, however, such an event was akin to losing a child. Trying to summon up a reasonable expression of concern, I enquired when it had last been seen.

"Well, that's the odd thing Sister. She was here for her breakfast, then she went out and when she came back she sat on your lap for a bit, didn't she Bert?"

He nodded his head solemnly in agreement.

"But that can't have been that long ago," I opined. "She's probably just popped out again."

"Oh no, she never goes out again till lunchtime. Always drapes herself across one of the pieces of furniture or on the back of Bert's chair."

"She can't be far," I hazarded unhelpfully.

"We've looked everywhere, haven't we my dear?"

I rather thought that Bert's contribution to this exercise would have been pretty minimal, but refrained from saying so. Anxious to get on with my task, I set out the dressing pack on the table and went to get the clean bandages from the bureau. Pulling down the desk top I fell back in shock as an angry ball of indignant black fur shot out and flew across the room.

"Blossom, you rascal, so that's where you were hiding," Mrs. Hodges exclaimed in satisfaction. "Poor Sister, you're having quite a day aren't you?"

"Let's put it this way," I said, "I don't think my heart will stand many more untoward incidents today."

Giving a laugh she replied," You know what probably happened, don't you?"

"I have no idea."

"When I rolled the bandages this morning and pulled the front of the bureau down in order to put them away, she must have crept in behind my back. Proper little character she is."

I had words a little less charitable with which to refer to the feline menace.

"Just think Sister, it was a real blessing you coming today, because without you we wouldn't have known the ramp was unsafe and we'd never have found Blossom, would we Bert?"

"Give me strength," I muttered to myself when I eventually returned to the haven of my car. "Give me strength."

Needless to say, no such episodes are ever likely to confront the nurse working in a hospital.

Chapter Six. A Cut Above The Rest

 Fortunately, or unfortunately, depending on how you viewed it, my practice contained more than its fair share of titled people and retired senior members of the armed forces and judiciary. Some of them had originally been private patients of Dr. Standish, but when he retired, the decision was taken by the remaining partners to accept only National Health patients. Whilst a little disgruntled, most opted to remain with the practice and bore with varying degrees of fortitude the indignity of having to wait their turn in the waiting room with everybody else. Many solved the problem by putting forward the need for a house call, which rarely proved to be justified.

During my years in hospital I had never enjoyed the time spent on the private wards, where some considered that simply because they were paying for the consultant they had bought the services of the nurse as well. It is also truly extraordinary the effect that a whiff of a title, or a handle to a name, can sometimes have on people.

One night, the paediatric houseman appeared in my office and asked if he could use the phone. He felt it inappropriate to talk in front of the parents of a child that had been admitted to the children's ward. His senior consultant answered with commendable promptness and listened to the young doctor's somewhat excited concerns.

It transpired that the son of a member of the local nobility had arrived at the casualty department in mild status asthmaticus, which had apparently been speedily and successfully dealt with, and the child taken to the paediatric unit. This information was duly relayed and, as the crisis had now passed, it was not unreasonable for his boss to enquire as to precisely why he was troubling him in the night hours. On suggesting that, as the patient was the son of a lord the houseman thought he might want to attend in person, he was told in no uncertain tones to remove the silver spoon from the boy's mouth, place it under his pillow and put it back in the morning.

Know Your Place Sister

I was none too happy when, just as I was looking forward to leaving the surgery at the end of the day, the receptionist informed me that a patient had been discharged from the private ward and needed to be seen that evening.

"What's the problem?" I asked.

"The message simply said that she had received extensive bowel surgery and has a leaking wound and a colostomy. The nurse said that they'd sent her home with enough dressings to tide her over."

Far from pleased, I made my way back to the town I had left only a short while ago in search of the patient in question, Primrose Arthur. The house proved to be an unattractive late Georgian edifice facing directly onto the pavement. I wasn't fooled as, over time, I had learned that there were some really amazing interiors hidden behind unlikely facades, although this wasn't one of them. In answer to my ring the door was eventually opened by a smallish woman in an apron who, I later learned, was the housekeeper.

"Come in," she said, "they're expecting you."

I stepped from the miniscule entrance hall into a lounge of quite gracious proportions and with the faded décor and furniture of a once splendid glory. This was nothing new to me, as I frequently discovered former members of the gentry trying to maintain previous standards of living in somewhat straightened circumstances and endeavouring to keep up appearances.

Seated in an armchair was a woman of 77, looking pale and unwell, clad in an apricot-coloured negligee. By her side sat a gentleman who rose to his feet saying, "I presume you're the nurse from the surgery."

"Yes, I am Sister Robertson," I replied with some emphasis on the title. Let's get one thing straight from the start, I thought. "And you must be Mrs. Arthur," I smiled, addressing the woman.

Her first words were hardly endearing.

"You know Sister, this really isn't a very convenient time to call; we're just having our pre-dinner drinks."

Feeling my hackles begin to rise, I responded in a quietly controlled voice. "I'm so sorry about that. Unfortunately I do have other patients to see and when I finish here I have to travel another six miles. I don't know when I'm likely to get my dinner."

Fixing me with a decidedly cool stare Primrose Arthur placed her glass on a side table. "Very well, what do you want to do?"

"I need to look at your dressings so that I can order future supplies. I'll also attend to your wound."

"That means going upstairs to the bedroom," she sighed, "how tiresome."

Slowly getting to her feet, she made her way across the room to a staircase. Placing her hands on the banister rails she said, "Mind you walk close behind me in case I fall. I want something soft to land on."

"Don't worry, I'm right here," I assured her through gritted teeth.

She led me into a single bedroom quite pleasantly furnished with definite feminine touches. The first things that caught my eye were numerous framed photographs of members of the Royal family, all of which were signed.

Letting her negligee fall to the ground she positioned herself on the bed.

"All the dressings are in a box in that corner," she said.

It soon emerged that this unfortunate lady had a very nasty mid-line abdominal incision which was leaking a foul looking discharge from a small sinus. To the left hand side of the incision was a bag fixed over a colostomy.

"I refuse to look at it Sister, and as for dealing with it don't even ask. They tried to teach me in hospital but it's all too disgusting."

"Well. It doesn't seem to require changing now," I said.

"Neither should it, they did it just before I left and that is how it will remain until your visit in the morning. I shall also require a bath," she added imperiously, as though she were ordering breakfast at the Ritz.

I set about dressing the wound, only too aware that a difficult and long road lay ahead. With everything in place I helped her up and she stood poised beside the bed with her arms outstretched.

"My robe if you please Sister. Then if you can find a sanitary towel perhaps you would undo it and leave it ready on the bedside table for later."

Dutifully I complied, making a mental note that I would never be any good as a lady's maid.

Once downstairs again I prepared to take my leave.

"Before you go Sister, perhaps you can tell me what time to expect you in the morning?"

"I'm afraid I can't be precise, Mrs. Arthur."

"You're not very well organised are you?"

"I don't think you appreciate that besides being the district nurse I am also the midwife. If I am called to a confinement I'm sure you understand that has to take precedence." As the lady in question had never had any children, I'm not sure that she did.

"However, I do have a staff nurse and a nursing auxiliary on the team and I will get them involved as well as soon as I can."

And that won't happen quickly enough I decided, as I eased myself into the car. Little could I then know quite how long Primrose Arthur would remain as a patient, nor could I foresee the impression she would make. However, it soon became evident that the natural curiosity of some team members would have to be quelled.

One of the nursing auxiliaries, who had been introduced in order to help her bath twice a week, returned to the surgery rather put out. "I was only showing an interest in all the signed photographs in her room," she said, and Mrs. Arthur became extremely curt and frosty.

Patiently, I had to explain that certain things were 'off limits' and that was one. "Any members of the Royal family, however minor or far removed, choose their friends very wisely. They can only hope to retain any privacy in their lives if respect and complete discretion are guaranteed by those within their circle."

"But I was only showing an interest," Dilys protested.

"No you weren't," I retorted. "You were being curious and curiosity killed the cat. Consider yourself well and truly dead!"

In spite of everything, as the months progressed, the nurses became quite fond of Primrose. We all grew used to her foibles and demands and learned to cope with them. Nevertheless, although she took considerable interest in our lives, families and problems, she remained totally unforthcoming about her own.

The day came when grief inadvertently caused her mask to slip. The staff nurse called one morning only to discover that Mr. Arthur had suddenly, and quite unexpectedly, suffered a heart attack and died in the early hours of the morning. From that day on Primrose made no attempt to leave her bed and come downstairs, neither could she be persuaded.

"Quite frankly Sister, I don't see the point," she stated firmly. Her general condition was such that she couldn't even attend the funeral.

Two weeks later, as I was finishing her dressings, she looked at me and said: "Sister, I would be grateful if you could do something for me."

"And what is that?" I asked.

"My solicitor is coming down from London this afternoon. Naturally, he will dine with me this evening and the housekeeper is preparing a suitable meal." Primrose described the menu. "However, she is quite incapable of choosing the appropriate wines. That was something my husband always did." Turning to one side she took a key from the bedside table.

"This is the key to the wine cellar. I want you to go down and select a suitable bottle of red and white for me."

Promising to do my best, I went downstairs and located Mrs. Hunt who indicated the correct door. Opening it I descended into a vast cellar. Bottles of wine were racked in serried ranks from floor to ceiling, not only along the walls but also down the centre of the cellar, all covered with a film of dust. I had never seen anything like it, for there were literally hundreds of bottles. Where on earth did one start? My knowledge of wines was absolutely zilch and such niceties as nose, bouquets and vintages meant nothing. In common with most of my colleagues, 'plonk' was 'plonk' was 'plonk', to be consumed with relish regardless. Calling to the housekeeper I sought her help.

"It's no good asking me; I've never been allowed down there."

Cautiously I removed a few bottles, wiped them, and peered uncomprehendingly at the labels. I might just as well have been reading Chinese. Finally, after grabbing two, I returned to the bedroom to present my offering for inspection.

Carefully Primrose Arthur studied them. A moment passed before her pithy voice was heard saying: "Sister, you disappoint me. Clearly your education has been lacking for you really have no idea. These are wrong, wrong, wrong!"

Sighing heavily, she slowly swung her feet out of bed, slid them into her slippers and indicated that I should help her into her dressing gown.

"I can see that I shall have to do it myself and you'll have to come and support me," she ordered.

Painstakingly slowly, Primrose made her way unsteadily down the two flights of stairs. Once in the cellar she stood surveying the scene. In a voice full of emotion, she said: "What memories Sister. You see before you my husband's professional business life. He was a wine importer. Some of these came from Fort Belvedere when King Edward VIII abdicated. Such wonderful times we all had then," she added wistfully. "The weekends, the parties and dances... " She trailed off and, quickly pulling herself together, unerringly made her choice and gave me the bottles to carry. We slowly made our return and I settled her into bed. Not another word was said.

Some weeks later an article in a national newspaper caught her eye. "Sister, have you seen this?" she jabbed with her finger.

The account was about a man with a longstanding wound which refused to heal and who had solved the problem by using a paw-paw. Mrs. Arthur's incision had failed to respond to anything, including the very best honey. A probe had revealed a deeply tracking sinus and her surgeon had long since discharged her, claiming there was nothing else that could be done.

"What do you think? Shall we have a go?" Primrose was on a mission and, groaning inwardly, I agreed.

With the bit firmly between her teeth she set about procuring a paw-paw. Not any old fruit would do for Primrose, however. A week later I was presented with a paw-paw dispatched from Fortnum and Mason's. There it reposed on a delicate china plate complete with silver fruit knife. Over the week, slice after slice was pared off and reverently placed on the offending site.

I was not in the least surprised when the desired result was not achieved. At least we had tried.

On 28 August 1979 the headlines in every newspaper proclaimed the assassination, on the previous day, of Lord Louis Mountbatten, the 1st Earl of Burma, his young grandson, his daughter's mother-in-law and a local boy. They had all been on their annual summer holiday on his estate in Ireland and were enjoying a day's fishing. His daughter and her husband were badly injured.

When I arrived at Mrs. Arthur's she was lying on her side in bed, scanning the newspaper with a magnifying glass. Her eyesight had been deteriorating for a while and reading small print was quite an effort. A photograph of Lord Mountbatten stood in its usual position on her dressing table.

"The news is terrible isn't it?" I remarked.

"Terrible doesn't even begin to describe it, Sister. It is ghastly beyond imagining and totally unbelievable. Don't say another word because I don't even want to talk about it."

Consequently the entire treatment was conducted in silence and she barely acknowledged my departure.

It was another two days before my next visit and I found Primrose slumped down in the bed, a folded letter in her hand and the magnifying glass on the counterpane.

"Good morning," she murmured listlessly. "I'm not in the mood for conversation."

I had never seen her look so low. With the dressings completed I prepared to leave when a hand fluttered out to detain me.

"Can you spare me a moment, Sister?"

"Of course," I replied.

"Pull up a chair beside me and sit down." I duly complied.

"Would you be good enough to read this letter to me? I've got the gist of it but I can't seem to focus properly."

Taking the letter I opened it out. The address simply read: 'Mullaghmore, Sligo'. Quickly I turned to read the signature. It was from Earl Mountbatten and had been written the day before his death.

There was nothing remarkable in it, simply a communication between friends hoping that her health was improving and giving news of the family, what they had been doing and the pleasure of having them around him for the holiday.

I finished reading and returned the letter to her outstretched hand. Not daring to say anything I simply sat and waited.

"Thank you," she said eventually.

Appearing to reflect for a moment she looked at me with clearly moist eyes.

"They are such a wonderful family and I can't believe that any of this has happened. You see, I have known Lord Mountbatten practically all my life," she continued. "I remember when he bought his first motorbike and he took me for a spin on the pillion. It was all so carefree and such fun then," she sighed.

The conversation trailed off.

"You must go and get on with your work, Sister."

"I don't feel that I should leave you like this," I replied, rather ineffectually.

"Don't fuss. I shall just rest here quietly and think about the good times. At least those murderers can't take my memories away."

It came as no surprise that, following this incident, Primrose began to lose interest in life.

However, at the beginning of November she approached me with another request.

"Every year my husband used to take me out to celebrate my birthday, Sister. Clearly that won't happen now," she sighed. "Instead, I want you to book a table at a local restaurant for the nurses who attend me to have a meal, and I will pay for it. I would also like you to include Jane from the surgery. She's always so pleasant whenever I call. We've had some lovely conversations."

"That is most generous, Mrs. Arthur," I murmured in surprise.

"Oh, there are two strings attached," she said. "I want everyone to wear long dresses and you must get someone to take a photograph of you all, not only to prove it happened, but so that I can see what you all look like once you've shed those uniforms."

On 8 November, nine of us gathered in our finery at a noted restaurant on top of the cliffs overlooking the Channel. That day Primrose gave me a sealed envelope with a cheque for £100 pounds inside, a not inconsiderable sum in those days. We wined and dined exceedingly well and persuaded a waiter to take our photograph on an instamatic camera. This I placed in an envelope along with a receipt and the change. We all signed a thank you card and I gave it to the nursing auxilliary who was due to attend to her next day.

Meeting up with the team at lunchtime I was greeted by Dilys.

"My goodness, you're in Mrs. Arthur's black books. She has demanded to see you before you go home tonight."

"What's all that about? You did give her the photo and card, I hope."

"Of course I did. She didn't tell me what the problem is though."

Muttering under my breath I headed off to face Primrose. Entering her bedroom I cheerily asked where the fire was! In a voice that would have chilled a hot cup of tea, she gave vent.

"I am extremely disappointed in you, Sister, I expected better."

Totally bewildered, I opened my mouth to speak but, before I could do so, she went on.

"I have never been so insulted in my life, never."

"Mrs. Arthur," I said firmly, "I have absolutely no idea what you are going on about. What is it that I am supposed to have done?"

"I gave you a sum of money to be spent on the nurses."

"Which I did," I interjected. "We had a wonderful time as I'm sure you have been told and is backed up by the photograph. We were all most grateful."

"Yet you had the temerity to send me a receipt and the change as if it were some commercial transaction."

Looking at her quite steadily, I said, "Mrs. Arthur, clearly I have committed a major social gaffe in your eyes but I must now make one thing quite plain. There is a rule that forbids nurses accepting money from patients. I decided that as your cheque had been given for a specific purpose there was no problem. The difficulty arose when there was more money than was required. I needed to be able to account for it in some way. I couldn't just pocket the change."

"Good heavens, have you no wit? Couldn't you just have bought a bottle or two of wine and kept it for you all to have at Christmas?"

"It didn't even cross my mind to do so," I said.

"Your honesty is commendable but boring, Sister. Take this change and do something with it and don't let it happen again."

With that, I considered myself well and truly dismissed and definitely not the flavour of the month.

Christmas came and went and it became obvious that Primrose was gradually fading. There was no change in her general state and she was pain free, but the will to live was no longer there. One morning, as we were going through the usual routine she said: "Do you believe in God?"

Somewhat surprised, I replied unhesitatingly: "I certainly do. My

Christian faith has always been very important to me. Why do you ask?"

"Well, my husband and I frequently attended church here until my operation. Since then I haven't been able to. The vicar did come to see me in the early days but, quite frankly, I wasn't in the mood."

"Do you want him to visit now?" I asked.

"I'm not sure. The old vicar's gone and I don't know anything about the new one. Do you know if he's any good?"

Smiling inwardly, I assured her that I had known him for some time. "I think you'd both get on well," I added.

Silence reigned for a moment before Primrose responded in her usual imperious tone: "Right Sister, go and arrange it for me. Give him my phone number and tell him to contact me to make an appointment."

A few days later she announced that the gentleman concerned had visited.

"You were quite right," she mused. "He's just my sort of person. We got on extremely well."

Relieved that I hadn't misjudged things, I was just preparing to leave when she stopped me in my tracks.

"He asked me if I would like to receive Holy Communion and I agreed provided that you are there. You will be, won't you?"

Thus it was that I was privileged to share in another very personal moment in the unusual life of Primrose Arthur.

A few weeks later this remarkable lady slipped peacefully from this world.

The local church was packed for her funeral service. Standing together were six members of the nursing team in uniform and Jane.

In 1976 a television drama entitled *The Duchess of Duke Street* was shown. It had been adapted from a book based on the real-life career of Rosa Lewis, the 'Duchess of Jermyn Street', a celebrated cook who ran the Cavendish Hotel in London. In the book Primrose's name appears as a young heiress with a reputation for being 'fast and fun-loving'. It was claimed that no party could truly be said to have started without her presence.

This then was 'our Primrose' who had so dominated the lives of a group of district nurses in the late '70s.

Several weeks after her funeral a letter dropped through my letterbox. It was from a firm of solicitors and contained a very generous cheque. Primrose had included me in her will. Other team

139

members and Jane, the surgery receptionist, were also remembered.

I was dumbfounded. With some of the money I bought my first fully automatic washing machine. Whether my patient would have approved is open to question. Primrose had been a vivacious, party-loving character, full of *joie de vie*. Such mundane utilities wouldn't have been at the top of her wish list. To call this item 'Primrose' was akin to heresy, but it made a huge difference to my life just as she had made an impression on all who came into contact with her.

A Crusty Colonel

Colonel Woods wasn't actually my patient, but he came under my care on alternate weekends when his own nurse was off duty. He lived alone in a pleasant house, almost on the coast, at the furthest limit of my patch. One wall of his living room was full of military books, and memorabilia of his career abounded. Once tall, but now becoming stooped, he still managed to cut a commanding figure.

He was quite a pleasant man, but his lack of any sense of time or urgency nearly drove me to distraction. The weekends, when we were effectively covering two patches or more, were always pressured and most patients did their best to be ready for us. Not so the Colonel. I would invariably arrive to find him way down the bottom of the garden, from where he made a slow and ponderous return. This would be followed by the need to wash his hands. Almost seated in his chair, he would then remember that he needed to go to the toilet. Finally, he would pronounce himself ready for the dressing procedure to begin, only to discover that his clean bandages were still hanging in the kitchen. His home help dutifully washed them but, like all patients, he was encouraged to take some responsibility by seeing that they were rolled up and ready for use.

"If this was a military operation," I said, "the enemy would have advanced and overpowered us before you'd even got everyone in position."

"Rubbish Sister, preparation, anticipation and alertness were my watchwords," he expostulated.

"Well. They clearly aren't now. One of these days, Colonel, you are going to drive me doolally tat," I stated in exasperation.

His head came up immediately and fixing me with an interrogative look, he barked: "Doolally tat! What do you know about it?"

"Nothing, except that you're determined to drive me there," I quipped.

"Come from a military family, do you?" he persisted.

"Certainly not, unless you count three uncles who served with the army in India in their youth, that is. Oh, and my father went to France with the D-Day landings."

"Did he by Jove?" he exclaimed, all antennae quivering. "What outfit was he with?"

"The Inns of Court Regiment," I replied.

"Fine regiment. Fine regiment. Knew their Colonel well. Cavalry of course."

"It may have been cavalry once," I said, "but it became part of the 21st Armoured Division. The only horsepower my father came across was under the bonnet of a Daimler armoured car."

Pulling himself up in his chair he returned to the original theme. "Why did you refer to doolally tat? Do you know what it means?"

Concentrating on bandaging his leg, I informed him, "It's what my dad used to say if I was sending him round the bend."

"Yes, yes, I know all that but do you know where it originates from?"

"I haven't got a clue," I replied cheerfully, "but I feel sure you're going to enlighten me."

"Doolally tat is a relic of British Colonialism in India. Deolali was a port there where ships arrived to transport the men back to England after finishing their tour of duty. The British Army also had a transit camp there to accommodate men who had gone mad after contracting 'camp fever'," he finished triumphantly.

Straightening up, the dressing completed, I replied: "Exactly as I said, Colonel, Deolali tat."

"Sister, you should never use expressions unless you know where they come from," he admonished.

"Yes Colonel." I saluted smartly and picked up my bag. At the door, I turned round and grinned at him, saying: "I can now safely say, with complete knowledge and full authority, that you will drive me doolally tat!"

Summoned To The Quarter Deck

Commander Andrews and his wife lived in a substantial house in a sought-after avenue in the town. Far from being commanding he was actually a quiet man. Of his naval exploits I knew nothing.

If he didn't appear particularly assertive, the same could not be said of his wife. The home was immaculate, highly polished and tastefully furnished and she was always smartly dressed and beautifully made-up with never a hair out of place. She also had the irritating habit of answering questions on her husband's behalf and always referred to him by his rank. "The Commander is in the lounge," or "the Commander will be down shortly," she would greet me. I came to the conclusion that service wives were often far more status conscious than their spouses.

The Commander was suffering from Paget's disease, which is a condition affecting the bones causing them to become weakened and deformed. Often it is the pelvis and spine which are involved and the pain experienced is usually worse when lying down. There is no cure, but symptoms can be controlled by painkillers and a range of medication to help regulate bone growth. A drug had recently come on the market which sounded promising, but it had to be given twice a day by deep intramuscular injection.

It was my custom to administer this at ten in the morning and six at night and initially all went well. Having watched my patient struggle with the stairs I suggested that perhaps it would be easier to give the injections downstairs.

"Really Sister, I don't think we want the Commander dropping his trousers in the lounge," his wife said, in a voice that would crack glass.

"Perhaps the dining room would be suitable," her husband proposed hopefully, clearly keen to remain on one level.

Tutting under her breath, she showed me through to a room which was dominated by a table so highly polished that you could see your face in it.

"Goodness," I said, "if I am to lay my things out, I really would appreciate a cloth to cover the table, please."

"You are on no account to put anything on the table," she ordered.

Casting round for another solution, I suggested that I could manage by putting my case on a chair.

"Very well, but wait until I've fetched a magazine for you to place

142

it on." I began to feel very sorry for my patient.

One morning as I was preparing to leave she said: "I'm afraid it won't be convenient for you to visit at six o'clock tonight, Sister. You'll have to come at nine."

Taking a very long breath, I replied quietly, "I'm so sorry, I regret that will be completely impossible. We do not have an evening nursing service except in an extreme emergency."

"But this is an emergency," she persisted.

Raising my eyebrows, I questioned what it was.

"Well, this is our bridge party night. Our friends will be arriving at three and when we've finished there will be drinks, followed by an evening meal. The very earliest we shall be finished is nine o'clock."

"Mrs. Andrews," I said, in as controlled a voice as I could muster, "I rather think you will have to decide which your priorities are. However, don't worry. It will do no harm if the Commander occasionally misses one."

"Thank you Sister," he quietly interjected, "you have simply confirmed what I thought. I'll see you tomorrow."

Arriving back at the surgery later in the day I found Dr. Chase writing some letters. Swivelling round on his chair he fixed me with a look. Shaking his head sadly he said, "Dear, dear, what are we going to do with you?"

"What have I done now?" I groaned.

"Well, apparently you've upset the good Commander Andrews or, to be more precise, his wife." In a wheedling tone he continued: "After all, they only wanted your visit deferred until nine o'clock."

Opening my mouth to reply, he held up a finger. "Surely that's not an unreasonable request. Where's your sense of vocation?"

Preparing to launch a fusillade, I caught sight of Jane laughing.

Dr. Chase returned to his writing, saying: "Worry not, for I duly defended your name and your reputation to the hilt. That woman really is outrageous. Thank goodness I'm not married to her."

The receptionist whispered, "You should have heard him, he was marvellous. You see before you, Saint Chase, patron of nurses."

"Quite right," he said. "I shall now require complete subservience and periodic attention paid to my halo."

It was only one of many occasions on which the doctors unfailingly supported us.

The Brylcream Brigade

"Don't stand any nonsense from this one," said my colleague handing over her list of visits for the weekend. "I visited him this morning following his discharge from the private ward, having been requested to remove alternate sutures and dress the wound. Unfortunately, the incision really hasn't healed that well so I left them be. See what you think tomorrow?"

"What's the matter with him," I asked suspiciously.

"He's a retired Squadron Leader, very affable and a bit of a smooth operator I suspect, but his wife is something else."

"So, what's the problem with her?" I asked.

I had already noted that they lived in one of the historical gems in the town and I'd secretly been hoping for a chance to see inside.

"Well, I called this morning and knocked at the front door. The wife opened it, took one look at me and told me to go round to the tradesman's entrance."

I couldn't help grinning because of all the District staff, she was possibly the most upper crust and the product of an extremely good girls' boarding school.

"I wasn't having any of that," she continued, "so I asked her whether she expected the doctor to do the same."

"Of course not Nurse, he's a professional person," she had the nerve to reply.

"What was your response to that?" I questioned.

"I informed her that the name was Sister and that I was a professional in my own right. She didn't like it but at least she let me in."

"Good for you! Give me Joe Bloggs in his council house any day; at least I know where I am with him."

The following morning I duly presented myself at the house and, feeling as though I was about to storm the battlements, knocked firmly on the very impressive ancient oak door liberally studded with ironwork. It was opened by a woman clearly of the twin-set and pearls brigade.

"Good morning," I trilled cheerfully. "I'm Sister Robertson. Isn't it an absolutely glorious day?"

"You'd better come in," she said, disdainfully refusing to acknowledge my greeting.

Stepping over the threshold onto the very old stone-flagged floor,

I prepared to follow where she led only to be brought up short.

"Would you mind removing your shoes and leave them on the door mat?"

Without apparently turning a hair, although the hackles on my neck were beginning to rise, I responded. "Not at all Mrs. Emery, if you will kindly supply me with some slippers."

Gazing at her decidedly neat little feet I felt it extremely unlikely that she could furnish me with anything that would accommodate my size 8s."

"I'm afraid I can't," she sighed, gesturing me into a long, narrow and very basic kitchen. "But please don't make a noise because the dog's had a stroke."

"I can promise you that I'm not in the habit of clomping round like the noble army of martyrs," I assured her. Passing an extremely lethargic looking spaniel spreadeagled in a dog basket, I dutifully tiptoed by.

"My husband is on a bed in the morning room," she announced, opening the door into a light, pleasant room with French windows looking out onto a beautiful garden.

The Squadron Leader proved to be rather a jolly man sporting a vividly patterned pair of Bermuda shorts. His wife speedily withdrew and left us to it.

I deemed it safe to remove alternate sutures and cleaned and redressed the wound. Just as I was finishing his wife reappeared saying in a querulous voice: "Are you likely to be much longer Sister, because the dog wants to pee?"

She must have seen my look of puzzlement and added, "I need my husband to carry him into the garden and support him while I hold his back leg up."

The gentleman duly sprang into action clearly totally heedless of the fact that, following his hernia repair, he wasn't supposed to do any lifting for a few weeks.

I quickly gathered my things together and made my escape before the remaining sutures gave way and the wound popped open.

People really are extraordinary, I concluded.

A Large Gin and Tonic

One of the drawbacks of being a district nurse is the fact that you are never completely 'off duty'. If you actually live within your patch it is amazing the number of people anxious to claim you as a friend in an emergency. The Good Samaritan was lucky he only had one casualty to deal with!

My modest modern house was somewhat inappropriately surrounded by buildings of great antiquity and was clearly erected at a time when planning laws were considerably more relaxed. On the opposite side of the road was a 15th century house which stood on the site of the country manor of former Archbishops. Until fairly recently it had echoed to the sounds of a young family who were heirs to an Irish peerage, who had settled in Kent during the 1920s. They had all grown up and moved elsewhere within the locality, leaving only the widowed dowager in residence.

Her ladyship wasn't that many years my senior and over the years I had come to know her fairly well. Very chatty and lively, she was also quite unrealistic, fey and impractical.

Responding to the ring of the phone one evening, I heard her voice apologetically asking me if I could possibly just pop over with some dressings as she had cut herself.

"It would be simpler if you came here where I've got everything to hand," I suggested.

"I can't possibly do that," she replied, "I haven't finished feeding the animals. I'll leave the front door open for you so just walk in," she said cheerily and put the receiver down.

Gathering a few steri-strips, dressing packs, pads and micropore tape together I duly shot across the road and entered the vestibule which led into an ancient stone-flagged dining hall.

"I'm in the kitchen," she called and I went through to be confronted with a scene of mild disarray. The sink was full of pots and pans and the table was covered with a miscellany of objects. By it stood her ladyship, hair falling over her face, feverishly trying to fork the contents of numerous cans of dog and cat food into various receptacles, while the expectant recipients either sat in readiness or wound their way sinuously in and out between her legs.

These actions were considerably hampered by a towel wrapped round her arm which was holding something of considerable bulk in place. Down her hand ran a steady trickle of blood to join the congealed pools already on the table. Pushing her somewhat peremptorily into a nearby chair, I placed her arm on the table and unwound the towel to reveal a very large bag of frozen peas. But on removing it a neat jet of blood shot into the air and I hastily replaced them.

"For heaven's sake," I exclaimed, "you've severed an artery in your wrist."

"Have I really, dear? It simply wouldn't stop bleeding you know."

"Neither will it until it's been tied and stitched," I said. "How long ago did this happen?"

"About half an hour I should think. "There's blood all over the freezer," she added inconsequentially.

"Never mind that, just listen to me. I am going to prepare a substantial pad of dressings to place over the wound but strapping it on won't be sufficient; you will also have to apply considerable pressure to it and keep it up while I drive you to casualty."

"Oh, I'm sure there's no need for that, Ann. You can fix it."

"No I can't, so let's get whatever you need in the way of a coat to put round your shoulders, then sit here by the front door while I go and get my car. And whatever you do, don't release the pressure on that dressing,"

"I must just finish feeding the animals," she wailed plaintively.

"Damn the animals," I said in exasperation. "At the moment your wrist is more important."

"How tiresome," she sighed. "Shall we just have a little peep in case it's stopped bleeding?"

"Don't you dare, on pain of death," I threatened.

I covered the six miles in reasonable time accompanied by a stream of banal conversation from my passenger, none of which was related to the situation in hand. We might as well have been going for an evening out. All the while the dressing was becoming bloodier.

A friendly face in the shape of the casualty sister waved us through to a cubicle.

"I'll get the doctor to come and have a look. If it does need stitching, Ann, if you could get everything ready for him he can get on with it without you having to wait for one of us," she offered obligingly.

Her ladyship, now reclining gracefully on a couch, greeted the houseman with gracious enthusiasm and prepared to hold social court as if we were at a cocktail party.

Having received the result of removing the dressing well and truly between the eyes the doctor simply said: "Let's just get on with it shall we?"

The necessary repair was skillfully carried out to the accompaniment of a non-stop flow of desultory conversation. In an attempt to stem the vocal stream he suddenly said, "Perhaps you'd like someone to get you a drink?"

"Oh, that is kind," she said. "Could I have a large gin and tonic?"

With eyebrows raised and a look of total disbelief on his face, he replied: "I was thinking more along the lines of tea or coffee."

"Oh," she replied, "no thank you. I'll wait until we get back to Ann's. I presume you've got some gin?" she asked.

"Let's just get home first, shall we?" I replied, casting an apologetic look at the somewhat incredulous doctor.

Once back home, my husband dutifully catered to her liquid requirements then promptly went in search of one of her sons to come and take her in charge.

There was an unexpected 'thank you' present as a result of this escapade. Arriving home from work one evening Debbie informed me that her son had called with a brace of pheasants.

"Where are they?" I enquired.

"I've put them on a hook in the broom cupboard," she said with a shudder. "They're quite disgusting and I refuse to touch them."

Opening the door I gazed at the sad spectacle of two once magnificent birds dangling from a piece of twine tied round their necks.

"Oh grief, they're not plucked, and I can't do it. I wouldn't even know where to start," I wailed, with the typical attitude of the average 'townie'.

I really was extremely grateful for such kindness but gave equally profound thanks for our friendly village butcher who was happy to render the offering 'oven ready'.

I rapidly came to the conclusion that, happy as I was to deal with the more unsavoury innards and outards of the human body, I preferred animals and feathered friends to be suitably dressed and ready for the table.

The Stately Homes of England

Standing in a landscaped park with terraced lawns and beautiful gardens full of roses, wisteria, clematis and jasmine was a Grade II-listed Palladian house. A manor house had stood on the site from Tudor times but it was rebuilt in the early 18th century.

The titled occupants could trace their lineage back to the Norman Conquest and probably had more right than any others in the area to expect preferential treatment and yet they never sought it. As a result they had the respect of all in the surrounding community; similarly there was little that they wouldn't do for the villagers and their tenants.

Completely without side, and devoid of airs and graces, they both regularly attended the ancient local church and Her Ladyship was a keen member of the WI. Nothing and nobody escaped her attention. If someone was ill she would be among the first to visit and never arrived empty-handed. It was not unusual for me to be requested by the hospital staff to attend a patient in the village for after-care, only to find that the person in question had been scooped up and ensconced in a comfortable bedroom at The House in order to recuperate. Here there were no fleets of servants and her ladyship cooked, prepared tempting trays and climbed the many stairs between the kitchen and the bedrooms in order to minister to them.

As a result, over the years I came to know the family well and constantly admired Lady W.'s prodigious energy and abilities. Although undoubtedly happiest when out tending her beloved gardens, she was no mean cook and was constantly baking, preserving and conserving. She was certainly never idle. His Lordship ran the estate, which boasted a prize pedigree herd of cattle as well as acres of agricultural land and good shooting.

In the early '80s I had occasion to attend their youngest son following an operation for a particularly nasty perforated appendix. The wound had refused to heal once the drainage tubes were removed and I attended daily to redress the site. Arriving one day Lady W. said: "Ann, I hate to ask this but would it be possible for you to make an early call tomorrow?" Hesitating for a moment she continued by explaining: "I know you are used to dealing with matters of confidentiality, so I don't mind telling you."

"Goodness, that sounds serious," I remarked.

"Oh, it's nothing to do with the family," she smiled. "No, the fact is that unless you come early you'll be subjected to police scrutiny. I expect you know that Princess Diana is paying an official visit to Canterbury tomorrow."

Indeed I did, for the local media was full of nothing else.

"Well, the thing is that she's coming on here afterwards for tea."

"My goodness, how exciting," I exclaimed.

"Of course, it isn't public knowledge as it will be a purely private visit to the family. The two eldest boys knew her quite well before she married so we're taking the chance to have a bit of a reunion."

"Well, I certainly can't compete with that," I said. "Look, if I pad James's wound well now, it will probably last out until the following day."

"Oh no, do come as usual please."

Arriving shortly after nine and entering through the back door into the kitchen, I came upon Her Ladyship, sleeves rolled up, busily baking scones. Brushing the flour from her hands she said: "I'm glad you've arrived. You can come and tell me what you think of my efforts."

Following her along the corridor she stopped and opened the door into a gracious drawing room which overlooked the sweeping lawns of the Park. The most beautiful but understated flower arrangements were strategically place to enhance the proportions of a room that positively sparkled.

"It really is lovely," I said, "quite perfect."

Clearly gratified, she said: "I picked absolutely everything used from the gardens. I'm glad you approve because I'm secretly rather pleased myself."

"Well, you've every right to be," I assured her.

"Try and come at mid-morning tomorrow and I'll tell you all about it over coffee," she beamed.

Once again I had been privileged to share in another memorable moment.

Without doubt, few other jobs would afford the opportunity to rub shoulders with such an eclectic mix of people and characters and I treasure the recollections of them all, whatever their status.

Chapter Seven.
Awkward Customers and Colourful Characters

 Checking into the surgery just before lunch one Tuesday, I was intercepted by the senior partner on his way out. Never one for time-wasting niceties he launched straight in.

"Good! You're just the person I want, Sister. Be a dear and just nip round to see Old Clopper. The girls will give you the address," he said, airily waving his hand in the direction of the reception desk.

"Who," I said, to his retreating back, "is Old Clopper?"

Stopping abruptly in his tracks he wheeled round and fixed me with an aggrieved look: "For heaven's sake girl, you must know Old Clopper. Used to lead horses and break stallions."

"Fascinating," I murmured dutifully. "What exactly is his problem?"

Exiting through the door he called back over his shoulder: "He's just come over 'somewhat unnecessary' and needs a bit of help." With that, he was gone.

"What sort of diagnosis is that?" I demanded of the smiling receptionist.

"I'm afraid I can't be much help," Jane said. "He and his wife live at 2 The Almshouses. A neighbour phoned in to say he was 'off his feet' and Doctor Standish went straight round. Clopper is 'old village'. The chap's a bit of a character and Doc's got quite a soft spot for him. All his life has been spent working with horses."

"Which he clearly isn't doing at the moment, is he?" I replied somewhat unnecessarily. Glancing at the clock on the wall, I said: "I've got an hour before this afternoon's ante-natal clinic, so I think I'll pop round there now and see what I can make of it? Have you got his notes so that I can flick through them?"

"Sorry, Ann; Doctor's taken them with him."

"Oh well, off we go into uncharted territory. See you later and if I don't turn up for the clinic you'd better send out a search party."

The almshouses had been built to commemorate the Great War

151

and, during the intervening years, the bare minimum had been done in the way of modernisation. The road was deserted as I pulled the car up except for a council worker digging a hole in the road.

In response to my knock, the door was opened by an elderly lady of motherly proportions. "You'd best come in, Sister," she said. "Doctor's been and he told me as how you'd come and sort things."

Without further ado she shuffled in her worn carpet slippers towards the door of a double bedroom opening off the hall. Huddled in a crumpled heap in the middle of an iron bedstead under a pile of assorted, rumpled bedding was the figure of a once wiry, but now grizzled, little man. His eyes were closed and he gave no sign of awareness or response when addressed. His skin was grey, cool and clammy, his pulse weak and thready.

"I'm afraid he's wet the bed Sister and there's no way I can move him," his wife whispered apologetically.

Wonderful, I thought. If this was Doctor's idea of 'coming over unnecessary' I didn't think much to it!

"Don't you worry Mrs... I paused quickly as I realised I didn't even know the proper surname. I hardly thought it likely to be Mrs. Clopper. "We'll soon make him more comfortable," I said with more assurance than I was feeling, having quickly ascertained that he was floundering in the middle of every nurse's nightmare, a feather mattress.

Incontinence sheets and pads and a urinal were hastily gathered from the boot of the car and, with the provision of a washing-up bowl of hot water, soap, sponge and towels I set to repair the damage. Beautifully ironed clean sheets and pyjamas appeared and by dint of rolling and manipulating, all was duly achieved. Throughout the entire procedure Clopper remained dead to the world, completely unresponsive. Whilst washing him I soon detected that his left arm and leg seemed quite weak and suspected that he had suffered a small stroke. Things were becoming clear. The problem was that I badly needed to get him moved further up the bed and better positioned to facilitate his breathing but I required some assistance.

"I'm just going to get some help to lift him," I told his hovering wife, and strode out of the front door coming to a halt beside the young man busy digging his hole.

"I could use a bit of your muscle," I announced to the somewhat startled figure. "Put down that spade and come with me."

Clearly not knowing quite what had hit him he tentatively

followed in my wake. Faced with the scenario in the bedroom he looked uncomfortably around him obviously wishing he was somewhere else.

"Now," I said, "between us we are going to lift this gentleman up the bed. I need you to stand on one side, and I will kneel in the middle. Put your hands under his body until they meet mine and grip them firmly." Gingerly he complied. "Good. Now, I am going to count, and when I say 'three' we will move him up the bed."

I suppose that it was a forlorn hope that all would go smoothly. My assistant clearly couldn't wait to return to an environment in which he felt more at ease. I had barely got to 'two' when an almighty heave on the part of my companion shot Clopper up the bed, causing me to lose my balance and fall inelegantly across the patient's inert body. From his now elevated position on the pillows Clopper's previously unheard voice suddenly growled: "Get off yer bugger!"

As I struggled to regain my equilibrium a rather desperate workman said: "Can I go now Sister?" And go he indeed did, for it was several days before he returned to the vicinity of his hole in the road which remained coned off.

Deciding that I had done the best I could for the time being I left for the ante-natal clinic, which I shared with another midwife whose sole responsibility was midwifery. Relaying the saga to her I bemoaned the fact that I would have to return to Clopper with another pair of nursing hands in order to settle him for the night.

"Tell you what," she replied. "I haven't got anything else to do when I've finished here, so I'll come with you now. It'll be a change from babies, bosoms and women's nether regions."

Gratefully accepting her offer we set off in tandem for The Almshouses. Clopper was in his previously comatose state and had again managed to wet the bed, although the incontinence sheets and pads had done their job well. Faced with once more getting his recumbent form higher up the bed my colleague announced that this time she would kneel in the middle and I could stand at the side. She was a trim and not unattractive blonde. Wriggling her hands underneath his body, ready to make contact with mine, our eyes met as suddenly her pained voice demanded: "Would you mind removing his hand?" Glancing down I could scarcely refrain from grinning as I saw Clopper's right hand snaking up under her dress.

"There's life in the old dog yet," I murmured.

"It's not that I mind you understand," she said, "but his hands are freezing!"

The patient rested against his pillows, eyes tight closed but with a look of peaceful satisfaction on his countenance.

Clopper only lived for three more days but I like to think he died happy.

The Uncrowned Village Queen

Although most patients are generally compliant and grateful, human nature being what it is, there are inevitably those who present something of a challenge, and would try the patience of Job.

Calling in at the surgery one morning, one of the receptionists handed me a piece of paper on which was scribbled a name and address and instructions to dress a small but persistent leg ulcer. "Use whatever means you think will be most effective," the doctor had written. "This lady is in dire need of a knee replacement but the surgeon won't operate until the ulcer is healed."

"Right, I'll drop in there now as it's only round the corner."

Gathering together a varied selection of dressings and bandages I prepared to leave.

"Good luck," said Jane, trying very hard to keep a straight face as she caught the eye of her colleague.

Both receptionists had been born and bred in the village, attended the local schools, and once married they chose to remain living there. Their national knowledge and experience may have been limited, but when it came to local affairs they were truly a mine of information, which could often be very helpful. However, medical confidentiality was sacrosanct and they were equally quiet and discreet regarding the private lives of the patients, unless they thought their background knowledge would assist us.

"Is there something I ought to know about this Mrs. Driver?" I asked.

Smiling rather mischievously Jane demurely replied: "Now, you know we always leave you to make your own assessment of the patients without being influenced in any way. Off you go and see what you think."

The lady in question lived in a late Georgian house that fronted straight onto the High Street in the centre of the village. From the window of her lounge she had a very good view of the 'world and his wife', as she sat in her winged armchair from which she would rise only to hobble to the kitchen for food, or to the cloakroom to relieve the other relentless bodily needs. A large brass knocker announced the arrival of any visitors and a firm voice could clearly be heard, imperiously bidding me to 'Enter'.

Mrs. Driver was a woman of average height and fairly solid build. Her white hair was swept back from her face in an attempt at a chignon, from which multiple strands had escaped. A once smart silk blouse accompanied a skirt of dog-tooth check which had clearly seen better days and now gaped at the waist fastening. Around her shoulders was placed a crocheted wool shawl. A pair of slippers, chosen for comfort rather than looks, adorned her feet which rested on an antique stool. Penetrating eyes stared at me from behind a pair of glasses attached to a gold-coloured chain.

"Well," she said, "at least you have the merit of being prompt. Doctor Chase only left about an hour ago." The voice was somewhat overly refined and very precise. Indicating her leg around which had been wound a crepe bandage that was completely unfit for purpose and totally ineffective, she said: "Now let's see what you can do about this nuisance."

On examination Mrs. Driver exhibited a small, typical venous ulcer which she had been attempting to treat with her own particular potions, but without success.

"The first thing I am going to do is gently clean the ulcer with a solution of salt water," I explained. "I will cover this with a non-adhesive dressing which will aid healing, improve comfort and help to control the discharge."

Venous ulcers can be quite painful and I constantly admired the stoicism with which the majority of patients endured the various procedures. Not so Mrs. Driver! There was much dramatic huffing and puffing, flinching and wincing, accompanied by some accusing looks cast in my direction.

With the dressing in place, I produced a brand new compression bandage and proceeded to apply it from toe to knee. I was brought up short by an indignant voice telling me to stop.

"I haven't broken my leg, girl. You only need wrap a strip of bandage round it. And you haven't put any ointment on that ulcer."

Sitting back on my haunches, I eyed her steadily. "Mrs. Driver, let me explain one or two things to you. First, no amount of ointments, creams or powders will have any effect at all. Second, the reason you have acquired this ulcer in the first place is due to poor circulation and persistently high blood pressure in the veins of your legs because the valves inside them have stopped working properly. The success or failure of healing rests solely with firm compression bandaging. By merely wrapping a strip round the middle of the leg you were impeding the circulation which caused the puffiness above and below it. To counteract this and improve the venous return it is necessary to bandage from a joint to a joint."

"There's no need to give me a lecture woman, I'm not stupid."

Very much tongue-in-cheek I responded: "That is clearly obvious which is why, recognising your intelligence, I have taken the trouble to explain in detail what we are trying to achieve."

With her ego partly mollified she bade me to continue. I had always prided myself on my bandaging technique so, on completion of the task, I was somewhat taken aback by her verbal onslaught: "Do you call that bandaging? It is absolutely hopeless Sister. You'll have to take it off and start again because it's not right."

"What exactly is wrong with it?" I queried.

"It's far too tight, I can't possibly stand that."

Mentally counting to ten, I removed the offending article and started to rewind it. Out came a hand and seizing the bandage from me she rasped: "Good heavens, you really have no idea, have you."

Feeling my ire steadily rising but determined to retain control, I replied: "May I ask which of us is the qualified, experienced trained nurse?"

I certainly wasn't prepared for the prompt retort.

"Let me inform you now, that I was in charge of the Red Cross in the village during the war and I prided myself on our ability to transform the village hall into a casualty clearing station in two hours flat if needed. That's experience for you," she crowed triumphantly.

"And was it?" I asked, inwardly seething.

"Was it what?"

"Ever needed?"

"As it happens, it wasn't," she admitted.

Taking a deep breath I launched forth. "Mrs. Driver, I'm sure your reputed skills were excellent but they were never put to the test and I don't for one moment imagine that they encompassed the treatment of leg ulcers. I, however, do possess the necessary skills which have been tried and tested on many, many occasions."

I waited for the next onslaught but none came. Gently taking the bandage from her I finished rewinding it and once more firmly reapplied it. Collecting my things together I prepared to leave.

"I will be back tomorrow to check," I informed her. "Now, before I go are you satisfied?"

"I suppose I will have to be," she said with a sniff.

Her voice followed me into the hall: "I still say this bandage isn't right, though."

Somehow I refrained from slamming the front door and sped back to the surgery with steam escaping from my ears. One look at my face and both receptionists erupted into laughter. Dr. Chase looked up from writing out prescriptions and grinning said: "I take it that the uncrowned queen of the village was on form then?"

"The woman's impossible and insufferable," I shrieked. "I'll probably end up strangling her with her confounded bandages."

"Just do us all a favour and get that ulcer healed," he said.

It was only then that I learned quite what I was up against. Apart from her wartime exploits with the Red Cross, Mrs. Driver had for many years been President of the local Women's Institute and taught and judged cake-making and decoration at county level. As the widow of a prominent retailer she considered herself rather above the common herd and only slightly below royalty. Both Jane and Edna had come under her tutorship and admitted that they were terrified of her. "Everyone is," they confided.

"Well, this one isn't," I assured them, "so let battle commence."

For 16 weeks the skirmish continued with subversive acts and the odd truce. Gradually, I introduced other nurses from the team which relieved the pressure on me somewhat, and gave her ladyship the chance to become adept at trying to play one off against the other, albeit without result. She found herself up against a united force that she couldn't crack. Nevertheless, it was a bit wearing and I literally sung the Hallelujah Chorus on the day when the ulcer was finally pronounced healed.

Within weeks she was duly admitted to hospital for the long awaited knee replacement, scheduled for Friday the 13th. I suppose I should have twigged that this was some kind of omen but was certainly not prepared for the news when it came.

Arriving to conduct the Friday evening surgery session for the 'walking wounded' I found Jane and Edna nearly bursting to convey the latest bulletin.

"You'll be devastated to hear that the hospital phoned this

afternoon to say that Mrs. Driver died on the operating table."

Two pairs of eyes studied me waiting for a reaction.

"Too right, I'm devastated," I replied. "All that time and effort on our part and that's how she repays us. The old so-and-so's probably sitting on a cloud chuckling her head off at the thought of getting one over on us."

On reflection I had just one thing to say: "God help St. Peter!"

However, Mrs. Driver hadn't finished yet. When her will was published it was greeted with incredulity, not least by the vicar who had also suffered at the hands of that formidable lady.

"In the event of my death my body is to be cremated and I wish the vicar to strew my ashes to the four winds from the top of the church tower."

As it was well known that the vicar couldn't stand heights and could never be induced to ascend the said tower it was her opportunity to have one last sally.

As the news got round it was received with withering scorn by the former headmistress of the village school, who had good cause to remember several exchanges with Mrs. Driver regarding the behaviour of the local children.

"Is it true Sister?" she queried when I called to administer her monthly injection.

"Is what true?" I asked.

"All this nonsense about the disposal of Mrs. Driver's ashes?"

Grinning, I nodded my head.

"Silly old buffer," she scoffed. "But it will give me considerable satisfaction to think of her remains lying in the road and being run over by numerous vehicles, or rolling around in the hub-caps of cars!"

Several attempts were made to discover just when this event was to take place, for there were many in the community who were not at all keen to think that they or their washing could be contaminated by the relics of Mrs. Driver. The information was never divulged and when, or if, it ever took place is unknown – except to the vicar, presumably.

Getting Into The Habit

The Dawson family lived in a gem of a Grade II-listed Georgian house, with a sweeping, semi-circular drive. Mother, father and their two young sons had not long moved in before they were joined by an unlikely couple. Jean Dawson had two aged spinster aunts for whom she had generously agreed to take responsibility. The eldest, Agnes, was 98 whilst her younger sister, Martha, was a mere stripling of 89 and both were heavily dependent.

The home of 'the flying nun'

Martha was almost totally blind. Nevertheless, she could manage her own personal needs and was able to join the family for meals in the morning room adjacent to the kitchen. However, that was the most that she could be persuaded to leave her sister for. Agnes was, without doubt, the most important person in her limited universe, and she was her constant guardian and companion. Very thin, prim and precise, she constantly questioned everything that had anything to do with her sister's daily care and welfare.

Agnes was the complete opposite to Martha. In shape she resembled neither apple nor pear but an extremely sturdy potato of considerable weight. Her mind was not what it once was and her sight was dim but her eyes twinkled with a hint of hidden mischief. Whereas Martha's voice was a mildly querulous but constant sound,

159

Agnes seldom spoke unless to mumble an answer to a question in muted tones. She was, for all the world, like a contented hippopotamus happily wallowing in the shallows.

Prior to coming to live with the Dawson family, she had spent her life in a religious order of nuns and was always referred and deferred to as Sister Agnes. As the order declined in numbers and was faced with the possibility of closure, her own family stepped in to care for her in the inevitably limited time that was left.

Jean had prepared a beautiful ground-floor room to accommodate them. Conveniently situated opposite a bathroom, and with views onto the garden, they couldn't have been better catered for. However, it soon became apparent that Sister Agnes's personal needs required more than Jean could provide unaided and the District Nurses were asked to intervene.

Every morning the team were faced with hauling Agnes out of her bed and onto the commode, giving her a wash, getting her dressed and walking her across the room on a zimmer in order to sit in the armchair where she would spend the day in varied states of awareness. In the evening, the nurses would return to reverse the procedure. The challenge was to get Sister Agnes fully attired in her nun's habit, a nicety which apparently still had to be observed. It certainly added another facet to our work. None of us had been faced with a wimple before.

It didn't take long before we realised that a hoist was going to be needed if Sister Agnes was to be moved into and out of bed and across the room to her chair without any of us breaking our backs. One was duly acquired and it became a daily occurrence to witness this figure in full habit literally sailing across the room. She became known as 'the flying nun'. Fortunately Martha couldn't witness this spectacle for she would undoubtedly have considered it far too undignified.

Unluckily for us, the day came when the lifting mechanism decided to jam, leaving Sister Agnes in just her vest as she was being transferred from commode to bed prior to getting her dressed. In vain, the pair of us struggled but the wretched thing would move neither up nor down. Slipping out of the room I found Jean and her husband and explained the position.

"Do you think you could bring a spanner or something and see if you can sort it out?" I asked.

"Certainly, I'll have a go," Bruce agreed.

"There's just one thing," I added. "Sister Agnes has only got a vest on, although we'll try to make her as decent as possible."

Addressing her husband, Jean said, "Whatever you do, don't dare open your mouth and say anything. You know what Martha's like regarding Agnes and her dignity and she'd have a fit if she thought a man was anywhere near while she was in her underwear."

We all trooped into the room where Martha had clearly sensed that something untoward was up and demanded to know what the problem was.

"It's quite alright," Jean said soothingly. "The hoist we use to lift Agnes is stuck and Sister's just come to get a spanner to repair it."

"Oh dear, oh dear," Martha wailed. "Whatever shall we do?"

"You are not going to do anything," Jean replied firmly. "Just sit there and let the nurses sort it out."

Meanwhile Bruce had crept in on slippered feet and was wrestling valiantly with the mechanism.

We had positioned the hoist over the bed so that should it suddenly lower at least Agnes would land safely on the mattress.

"Where's Agnes now?" Martha persisted. "Is she warm? Agnes, what are you doing?" she demanded.

The usually unresponsive Agnes suddenly announced that she was swimming.

"Don't be ridiculous," her sister retorted crossly. "You're just being silly."

Whether Sister Agnes ever twigged that she had a man kneeling at her feet we never knew, but we all breathed a sigh of relief when she finally descended to earth in a reasonably controlled manner thanks to Bruce, his tools and some WD40.

A few days before Christmas, Sister Agnes celebrated her 100th birthday. It was mid-morning before we managed to arrive to get her up and, on the way, we had passed the Salvation Army band playing carols in the centre of the village. On mentioning this to Jean she decided to go and ask them if they would come and play on Agnes's big day.

They duly agreed and some came into the house whilst the others positioned themselves outside the windows. Seated in her chair she beamed beatifically while the band went through a repertoire of carols. Wishing her a happy birthday they eventually departed.

"There," said Jean triumphantly, "What did you think of that Sister Agnes?"

"Hadn't they got lovely voices?" she announced to our total bemusement, as they had simply played their instruments and hadn't sung a note.

Hymn singing, however, was something which Agnes liked to indulge in on occasion and we were all expected to join in. Amazingly she was invariably more word perfect than we were. One Sunday I was washing her as usual when she said, "What day is it?"

"It's Easter Day," I replied.

"We'd better sing something then," she declared.

"Alright, what do you want to sing?" I asked, mentally going through the range of hymns appropriate to the season.

Without hesitation, and her face completely devoid of expression, she announced: "How about *Roll Out the Barrel*?" Life with Sister Agnes was never predictable.

The day inevitably came when it was deemed unwise to get her up and dressed. She was becomingly increasingly tired and incontinent. This presented another problem as we constantly fought to prevent pressure sores from forming on her ample buttocks, the skin of which was by now tissue-paper thin.

Day by day she became visibly weaker until she simply drifted peacefully away.

The flying nun had finally flown to higher realms.

Mental Infirmity

At one time it was accepted that most villages were cursed or blessed, depending on your point of view, with a resident eccentric who had become a part of local folklore.

Isabelle Manners had spent all her life in my home village. The youngest of three sisters, she originally lived with her parents in a prestigious house set in its own grounds surrounded by their orchards. In the early '60s everything was sold and a bungalow was built for them. Two sisters had already moved away and Isabelle went to university, graduating with a degree in science. Shortly afterwards she suffered what was referred to as a 'nervous breakdown' and she returned home to live. However there was already a history of mental problems in her mother's family, and she was eventually admitted to the psychiatric hospital.

Once discharged her behaviour became increasingly erratic and aggressive. Although she was of average stature, the frequent violent physical fights with her father became legendary. It is unsurprising that he died shortly afterwards, leaving mother and daughter to each other's tender mercies.

Possessed with dubious hygiene standards, and often bizarrely dressed, she was also cunning and sly with a vicious, mean streak. Children were terrified of her and everyone tried to give her a wide berth. This didn't suit Isabelle one little bit, and her actions grew to be more and more outlandish and difficult to contain as she sought to draw attention to herself. On top of everything else Isabelle had a complete obsession about gypsies who, she was convinced, were trying to kill her.

Nevertheless, there would often be periods of inactivity on her part which served to lull the community into a state of false security, only for matters to erupt again. People became convinced that this always coincided with the appearance of a new moon, when they would brace themselves to face the next round of Isabelle's actions.

Relative peace reigned for several months when she formed a liaison with the very diligent, local roadsweeper and whisked him home to live at the bungalow. Although quite a strong man, even he wilted under her constant assault and battery. Not surprisingly he eventually took himself off to seek employment elsewhere, after which the streets of the village were never as well tended.

Although there were many who privately considered Isabelle to be quite mad and in need of permanent psychiatric detention it wasn't as simple as that. Generally a person can only be sectioned under the Mental Health Act if two doctors and a social worker, or a close relative of the patient, believe it to be necessary. In this case there were no complaints from her family and no member of the public formally lodged a protest.

From a medical perspective her behaviour was not deemed to be such that she required sectioning and there is often considerable reluctance to go down this route if it can possibly be avoided. Isabelle, however, was on regular medication following her previous admission. In 1968 her GP managed to persuade her that this needed to be reviewed and to everyone's amazement, she agreed to be admitted to hospital as a voluntary patient.

About a year before my arrival on the district, Isabelle took her own discharge from the psychiatric unit and returned to her old haunts. Unfortunately, she didn't arrive unaccompanied having brought with her another patient with whom she had struck up a relationship. Lawrence was reasonably well-built physically but no match for the smaller Isabelle whom he dutifully followed like an obedient dog ready to do her bidding. From the perspective of the community they were double trouble.

My first experience of the havoc they could cause came after a night spent attending a home confinement. Arriving back in the village I saw my father standing outside the driveway to the church, seemingly scratching his head in bewilderment as he looked up and down the road. Bringing the car to a halt beside him I wound down the passenger window.

"What's up?" I asked.

"Just come and have a look," he replied, "you're not going to believe this."

I certainly wasn't prepared for the spectacle which confronted us as we walked up the church path. Either side stood the usual rows of graves; what wasn't normal was the sight of a pint bottle of milk solemnly placed in front of each headstone.

Dad's face bore the look with which I had become familiar on occasions when I had overstepped the mark. "I am very close to breaking the sixth commandment," he muttered, "and probably will if I can get my hands on that lunatic couple."

Ever since our arrival, Isabelle had set the new vicar and his home in her sights. She and Lawrence were forever banging on the door on some fatuous pretext or another, while their trademark annoying activities occasionally left an impression inside the church itself. Prayer and hymn books tidily placed on shelves would be distributed liberally in all the pews. Kneelers could be found piled up like so many building blocks into incongruous constructions. Slightly more worrying was their obsession with lighting every single candle they could lay hands on. As a precaution these were never left lying around and the vestry and belfry were kept locked, but it still left most of the place exposed to their antics.

Since their return home the pair had acquired a wooden truck on wheels which the long-suffering Lawrence was required to pull after him. It was piled with whatever possessions Isabelle decided to fill it with. On that particular morning they had walked the High Street in the wake of the milk float which made daily house-to-house deliveries between five and six o'clock. Whilst the occupants were still blissfully sleeping, the intrepid couple had loaded the bottles into their cart and redistributed them to some equally sleeping residents.

164

Dad and I made our way to the newsagent's shop, noting the people gathering in groups on the pavement clearly discussing the absence of any cow's juice.

"I'm afraid that if people want their milk this morning they will have to come and collect it from the churchyard," he informed the bemused proprietor. "Perhaps you'd be kind enough to let folk know and get them to spread the word."

"That pair gets dafter by the minute," grumbled one customer.

One or two more resilient hearts couldn't help seeing the funny side of it.

"I don't know, vicar. I always thought the New Jerusalem was supposed to be a land flowing with milk and honey. Perhaps you ought to tell them!" one quipped.

When I had taken up my new post I learned with dismay that Lawrence was registered with the practice. Isabelle remained with the village doctor who inherited her from another when she was struck off the books. Indeed, she seemed to be passed around between the medical fraternity like an unwanted parcel.

Shortly before eight o'clock one Sunday morning, the telephone rang. Mum answered it to hear Isabelle phoning from a call box.

"I want the vicar," she said. "Tell him to come right away, I've killed Lawrence."

Down went the phone. Fortunately I had already set out on my rounds. Mum dashed to church where Dad was just about to start the service and the message was hastily conveyed.

"If she really has killed him there's nothing much I can do," he replied. "If she hasn't, it will just have to wait until the service is over."

The churchwarden, who had known the family for years, announced his intention of accompanying him: "She's so unpredictable, it will be better if two of us go."

Up to the orchard they drove and finding the door of the bungalow wide open, tentatively ventured into the chaotic interior. There in the kitchen, slumped in a corner, was the figure of Lawrence looking even more dazed than usual. One eye was already showing signs of bruising while there was a steady flow of blood from a large cut on his head. Isabelle stood calmly surveying the scene.

"For heaven's sake woman, what have you done?" father exclaimed.

"He was being very silly," she pronounced decisively. "He

165

wouldn't do as he was told so I hit him over the head with a frying pan." There on the worktop was indeed a very substantial, heavy, cast-iron frying pan.

The churchwarden departed to phone for an ambulance while Dad endeavoured to find something to stem the wound.

"Why did you tell my wife that you'd killed Lawrence?" he enquired.

"Because I thought I had. You see he didn't move for ages," she responded smugly.

The victim was duly carted off to hospital concussed and wounded, but the ambulance crew refused point blank to allow Isabelle to accompany him. Their exploits had become common knowledge throughout the area. Their names were a byword to the police, and the bus company had already issued instructions that they were not to be allowed on board following a few untoward incidents.

Yet again it transpired that no further action could be taken, as Lawrence refused to make an official complaint. Although the police have the power to remove someone 'to a place of safety' for their own protection, or the protection of others, their incongruous behaviour was regarded as merely a nuisance and eccentric. There was never any evidence that they had caused actual damage to property or persons, other than to themselves.

Ten days later the couple presented themselves at the Vicarage requesting the vicar to remove the sutures from Lawrence's head.

"Isabelle, I am neither a doctor nor a nurse, nor is this a hospital or a surgery," he sighed.

"Well, go and get that girl of yours to do it," she demanded.

"She isn't here, so just go and do as I say."

In the event, the nurse in casualty had the pleasure of removing the stitches for which I was thankful. However, Isabelle was determined to get her own back for the inconvenience my absence had occasioned.

Every year the nurses could guarantee that we would be presented with one or two severe cases of herpes zoster, or shingles as it is more commonly known. This viral disease, characterised by a painful skin rash, travels along nerve pathways to affect a limited area on one side of the body. Small blisters form, which exude a serous discharge, and finally crusts over. Although healing eventually takes place, some sufferers experience residual neuralgic pain for months, and sometimes even years after.

More common among the over-sixties, poor Grace Waring had experienced a particularly debilitating attack. One side of her face, as well as her head and neck were all completely encrusted; her left eye was swollen and closed and the ear was similarly affected resulting in hearing loss. It was small wonder that, being in constant pain, this elderly lady took to her bed. She lived with her daughter Enid in a council house on the outskirts of a village and here she was most lovingly cared for.

One morning, whilst tending to Grace's multiple needs, I heard a loud knock at the front door. Her daughter appeared in the bedroom and, in a state of some agitation, informed me that Isabelle Manners wanted to speak to me immediately. Not best pleased, I left what I was doing sensing that Enid was only too anxious to get rid of this unwanted visitor.

"What do you want Isabelle?" I asked none too graciously.

"Your car is obstructing the Queen's highway. Come and move it immediately," she demanded.

"Don't be ridiculous. It is parked quite legally outside this house and is in no one's way," I retorted briskly.

"Well, it's in my way and is obstructing my progress," she announced firmly.

"In that case, you'll just have to walk round it. I am very busy attending to an extremely ill patient and I have neither the time nor inclination to play silly games."

With this I closed the front door.

"Don't worry," I assured the plainly nervous Enid, "she won't bother you. I'm afraid it's me she's got it in for," I said with a laugh.

I didn't know whether to be annoyed or amused when I left the house to discover that Isabelle had drawn a thick chalk mark on the road around my car, which clearly denoted a parking bay. Propped against the windscreen was a piece of cardboard bearing the words: *Nurse's car for sale.* Shoving it unceremoniously into the boot I heard the voice of the postman.

"You've certainly upset 'her ladyship' this morning Sister. Never mind, while she's harassing you at least the rest of us will be left in peace."

"Thanks," I said with a grin, "I always aim to help the community."

Once back in harness, this incongruous couple literally walked for miles each day over the fields and lanes and I frequently came across them in the most unlikely places. Isabelle, armed with a branch as a walking stick would stride out ahead, while Lawrence, laden like a pack animal, and always equipped with a kettle for brewing tea on their camp fire, patiently plodded behind. Although they had frequent fights and skirmishes, there was never any doubt as to who had the upper hand.

The worry for everyone was old Mrs. Manners who was totally at the mercy of her daughter. Sometimes she would be seen sitting in an ancient wheelchair, strongly resembling the Giles cartoon 'Grandma', as Isabelle pushed her round the village. Part of the concern arose from their antics on the hill leading down from the bungalow, where they would let go of the chair and leave it to freewheel while they careered after it laughing like children.

On another occasion, the couple left the old lady in the wheelchair parked outside the post office whilst they went off for the day. Furnished with a packet of sandwiches and a bottle of drink she seemed quite happy watching the world go by, and didn't complain or ask for help. Eventually she was duly collected and taken home.

It was a great relief when this family at last came to the attention of Social Services, who had an unenviable job and an uphill struggle to contain the situation. The old lady was finally taken into care and died shortly after.

Occasionally the Christian consciences of some local people would be pricked into action and one or two brave souls invited Isabelle into their homes to have a bath or a meal. However, they always became disillusioned as such generosity was simply taken advantage of and usually ended up with their guest virtually camping on the doorstep. It didn't take long for the milk of human kindness to stop flowing.

The shopkeepers in particular were very wary, especially when they began to detect signs of shoplifting. Needless to say it was the unfortunate Lawrence, undoubtedly instructed and egged on by the resourceful Isabelle, who was finally caught in a store in the city. As it wasn't the first time this had occurred he was sentenced to imprisonment.

Relative peace reigned once again, although Isabelle's silliness often emerged to amuse the village. She was an inveterate attendee at local jumble sales, where irritated stallholders would simply give her things in order to get rid of her. This resulted in her wearing a totally bizarre collection of clothing. After one such foray she marched round the area for a fortnight wearing two hats topped by a pair of knickers.

The day came when Lawrence was released from prison where he had at least been fed, bathed and his medication reviewed and supervised. Two days later, on a beautiful sunny evening, he appeared at the surgery in order to renew his prescription. Clad in shorts, with a knotted handkerchief on his head, he approached the receptionist to collect a numbered disc. The waiting room was virtually full and the occupants of one bench reluctantly moved up to make a space for him. Once seated, in a loud voice he said: "I've just come out of prison."

As a conversation opener it was a blinder. People fidgeted nervously and buried their heads even deeper in what they were reading.

"Do you know what I was in for?" he asked.

When it became clear that no one was going to respond, Lawrence decided to tell them anyway.

"I was sent down for raping the Queen," he proclaimed proudly.

Jane looked at me helplessly as I said: "For goodness sake do something. We can't endure a whole evening of this."

"Dr. Chase is only on his third patient and Lawrence is number 17," she replied.

Looking over the desk into the waiting room beyond we suddenly caught sight of Isabelle pulling faces at everyone through the window and waving her stick. Without any further delay Jane asked the assembled company: "I wonder if anyone would mind if this gentleman went in next?"

Never in my life have I seen so many people unanimously prepared to give up their place in a queue. The buzzer went, Lawrence was hastily ushered through and the previously silent patients rediscovered their tongues.

Coming to the end of my surgery session one balmy autumnal evening, two phone calls came in reporting that Lawrence had been spotted running around naked in the orchards adjoining their home. A quick check on his records revealed that he had failed to renew the prescription which kept him reasonably under control.

"He's going to need an injection to calm him down," Dr. Rivers decided. Both doctors had yet to complete their surgery sessions and I was ready to depart for home.

"I suppose you don't fancy going that way, do you?" they asked.

Looking at them fair and square I said: "I don't often refuse your requests but if you think I'm chasing a rampant, naked Lawrence round an orchard with a loaded syringe, you're sadly mistaken."

They both grinned before admitting that it had been a nice try but a forlorn hope.

One day it suddenly began to dawn on folk that Lawrence was now nowhere to be seen. Isabelle still strode around in her inimitable fashion but always on her own. Eventually someone plucked up the courage to ask her where he was.

"He's gone off on holiday," she declared.

Feeling that this was highly unlikely it wasn't long before the rumour spread that the lady had 'done him in', which wouldn't have surprised any of us.

It was with mixed feelings that we learned that a body, in an advanced state of decay, had been found alongside a hedgerow miles away in another county. Finally identified as being that of the missing Lawrence, an autopsy showed him to have died of natural causes. Whether he'd finally had enough and simply taken off will never be known.

Isabelle was as tough as old boots and we all firmly predicted that she would live to a ripe old age. To everyone's surprise, though, she suddenly succumbed to a chest infection and was admitted to hospital, where she died within days aged 73.

There is never an easy solution when faced with the many aspects of dealing with mental health problems. At one time Isabelle and Lawrence would undoubtedly have found themselves cast permanently into the hell of Bedlam. This infamous institution was replaced by large, depressing mental hospitals which dominated the landscape in the Victorian period. Although still operative whilst I was on the district, thankfully the latter part of the 20th century marked the beginning of the end of such establishments, and attempts are now made to manage the problem locally with the support of smaller psychiatric units and community psychiatric nurses.

No Lady Chatterley's Lover

Living in a substantial lodge house on the fringe of a wood was a retired gamekeeper. For years he had worked on Lord W.'s estate and had been allowed to remain in his tied accommodation once he retired.

George Fellows came to my attention in the mid-'80s with the all too familiar problem of oedematous and ulcerated legs. He was a bear of a man living in surroundings that left a lot to be desired. On my first visit I found him sitting by the window in a carver chair dressed in his ancient, tweed gamekeepers' breeches which had been cut up the seams to accommodate his swollen legs. On a dilapidated and threadbare chaise longue sprawled an ancient liver and white spaniel. Strutting delicately between the butter dish and marmalade jar on the table were a pair of chickens, pecking at the remains of the breakfast crumbs.

Having introduced myself I set about stating some ground rules.

"Mr. Fellows, if you want any members of the nursing team to attend to your legs those chickens will have to be consigned to the garden."

"They ain't doing no harm," he declared sullenly.

"I shall need to use that table to set out the dressings and I am not prepared to share it with poultry, nor chance the undoubted risk of infection which they certainly pose."

"You tell him Sister. I'm fed up with the dratted things messing all over the place."

My heart soared as I recognised one of the inestimable Home Helps who were provided by Social Services in order to meet the needs of those who could no longer cope with their domestic requirements. I frequently marvelled at their patience and tenacity, often in the face of somewhat unsavoury situations, and Glenys was no exception. As tall as me, but more comfortably proportioned, she was a hard worker and often went above and beyond the proverbial extra mile to help her clients, without regard to monetary reward. Incredibly cheerful and good-natured she was, but a pushover she wasn't.

From that moment on George realised what he was up against.

"You're a couple of right bossy boots," he grumbled.

"Well, someone's got to try and keep you in order," she replied, and promptly set about dispatching the clucking menaces.

Meanwhile I attempted to clean part of the table and explained to the patient what we would be doing.

"How long have your legs been like this?" I asked.

"Started three years ago, I reckon," he said.

"Why didn't you go to the doctor then?"

"Well, they weren't anything much and the wife reckoned she

could cope, so we got bandages and things and managed."

"She must have been a saint," I commented.

"She were a pretty good sort," he agreed, "but she got taken a few months back and I suppose I just let everything go."

Arriving with some clean socks for him to put on, Glenys chipped in: "What you mean is it all got too much for her. I reckon she needed my help then as much as you do now, but you both insisted on soldiering on."

"Well that's my way. I don't like a lot of people interfering," he asserted firmly.

Seeing me looking at a large framed photo hanging on the wall, George reverted to his usual banter.

"Good-looking chap isn't he Sister?"

I had to confess that the smartly uniformed soldier gazing down on us was quite personable.

"That were me," he said proudly. "Grenadier Guards I was in – the best regiment in the country. Did duty at Buckingham Palace, I did."

Looking at the grey stubble on his face and his unkempt appearance I wrinkled my nose and remarked: "If they could see the state of you now you'd be put on a charge."

"I'll shave when I want to," he said, defensively rubbing his chin, "unless either of you two feels like obliging."

"There's nothing wrong with your arms and hands," Glenys muttered.

"And I'm here solely to concentrate on your legs," I added.

"You do that Sister, and I'll concentrate on yours. They aren't half bad," he grinned.

Going to the kitchen in order to wash my hands, I found Glenys tackling his laundry.

"Thank goodness you've come," she said. "Perhaps we can get somewhere now."

"I don't know how you put up with it," I remarked.

"Oh, he's not too bad. Irritating, infuriating, awkward and obstinate old cuss he may be but for all his bluster he's harmless."

So began months of daily attendances in a battle to prevent George's legs deteriorating any further. Fortunately, by deploying the team equally everyone only had to suffer the situation for two days each week, unlike poor Glenys. By comparison, we had it easy. The verbal sparring matches were a regular feature and he was forever pushing his luck as he ladled it on thick with the younger, prettier nurses.

The day came when I finally lost my cool. Pulling up in the lane outside the Lodge, I was halfway up the muddy garden path when I was brought to a complete halt by the sound of a rifle shot which was too close for comfort. Looking up I was in time to see George's face grinning from the living room window out of which the unmistakable barrel of a weapon protruded. Incensed beyond belief I stormed into the room in time to see him returning the gun to its place in the corner.

"What the devil do you think you're playing at?" I shouted.

"Stop making such a fuss Sister, anyone would think you'd been hurt. I weren't aiming at you, merely taking potshots at the rats. There's a load of them out there at the moment. Anyway, I'd heard your car so I knew you were there."

"I don't care if there's an infestation of baboons," I raved, "you don't fire that thing when any of the nursing staff are likely to be in the vicinity or it will be the last visit you ever receive."

"Stop being such a Jessie," he growled. "I'm a first class shot and I don't need you to tell me how or when to handle a gun."

"I don't care if you're Davy Crockett, Wyatt Earp and Annie Oakley rolled into one," I retorted, "there is to be no more sharp shooting."

For some time I had been considering asking Dr. Chase to refer George to our friendly hospital consultant Dr. Lynton and this episode sealed it. In response to a formal request he agreed to carry out a domiciliary visit one Thursday afternoon.

The two men stood watching as I removed the dressings to reveal George's legs.

"Not a very pretty sight, are they?" Dr. Lynton said.

Straightening up he addressed George: "I think a spell in hospital is needed to try and improve these a bit, don't you?"

"Oh, there's no call for that doctor," he said. "The nurses are managing just fine."

"Indeed they are but I think a bit more aggressive help is needed in order to control the situation. It is unlikely that I or the nurses will ever heal these completely. The important thing is to prevent them from reaching the stage when you run the risk of losing one, or both of them."

"Never, doctor," said George incredulously. "They ain't that bad."

"At the moment no, but they're not far off it. I propose we take you in next week and see how things progress."

I could have flung my arms round his neck with gratitude. Even a week's respite would be heaven. Once assembled outside, I thanked him profusely.

"Quite frankly Sister, I don't know how you cope. It does me good to do a home visit at times in order to fully appreciate the problems. It's all a bit rustic without the charm, isn't it?" he remarked with his gentle smile as he surveyed the surroundings.

"You haven't seen the rats, nor the chickens on the dining room table, or been confronted with a shotgun yet," I grinned.

A letter duly arrived at the surgery two days later confirming that: 'Following the district nurse's royal command performance yesterday, I will admit Mr. Fellows to hospital on Wednesday'.

The one person who was possibly more pleased than anyone was Glenys. "Honest to God, Sister it's the best present I could have. With him out of the way I can really blitz that place."

"Surely you won't be paid while he's not here?" I queried.

"Don't you worry about that; I'll come in my own time if it means the chance to sort things out so that things are easier when he comes back."

George, however, was far less ecstatic. "What's going to happen to my dog and the chickens?" he demanded.

Glenys had the immediate answer to that.

"What about that drinking crony of yours? Oh yes, I know all about Ned's evening visits bearing liquid refreshment from the pub," she twinkled. "He was one of your gamekeeping pals, so another dog and a few chickens will hardly be a problem to him. Get it sorted," she ordered. "And while you're about it you'd better let me buy you some pyjamas and decent toilet stuff. You certainly can't go into hospital with those rags you persist on wearing."

"Heaven help your poor husbands," he sighed. "I can't imagine how they survive."

"Possibly because they don't give us such a hard time," I retorted.

Turning to Glenys, he grumbled: "I suppose you will want some money to buy all these things you seem to think I must have?"

"Well, I'm certainly not paying for them. Poor George, shall I get a crowbar to prise open that purse of yours?" she laughed knowingly.

There was no doubt that the pair of us both felt demob happy.

In the end George's stay in hospital lasted for five weeks. By the time he returned home the house had virtually been scrubbed from top to toe, in which endeavour Glenys had been helped by the redoubtable Lady W. Visiting The House one day for the purpose of attending to their youngest son, I found myself joining her and his Lordship for coffee round the vast kitchen table. Describing the ordeal facing Glenys at The Lodge nothing else would suffice than for her Ladyship to roll up her sleeves and pitch in.

"George is quite impossible," I moaned.

Quietly spoken and a man of few words, Lord W. rebuked me swiftly. "He was the best gamekeeper I ever had. Poachers certainly never took liberties when he was around."

Thanks to Dr. Lynton, George was followed up three monthly in outpatients and readmitted on two further occasions. The difference this made to the district nursing team was immense as they no longer felt that they were struggling ineffectually and in isolation.

Less than two years after I had retired, George died. There were no family members but the little church was full of estate workers past and present when he was laid to rest alongside his wife. For George, the icing on the funeral cake would undoubtedly have been the detachment of Grenadier Guards which her Ladyship somehow managed to arrange in order to fire a volley at the graveside.

Challenging and time-consuming as some patients were, and annoying and irritating though they proved to be on occasion, they each formed part of the rich tapestry that is District Nursing. Although I can by no means claim to be houseproud, without doubt, some of the unsavoury habitats I visited made me feel that I could safely enter my own residence in a competition for delightful Homes and Gardens, or even open it to the public.

Chapter Eight.
The Day Thou Gavest Lord Is Ended

 Sadly, a subject that was freely talked about in the Victorian era, or reluctantly accepted as the inevitable result of enemy action in the two world wars, had developed into something of a taboo. By the 1980s death had become sanitised as people sought to distance themselves from it by handing over care of the elderly and dying to the 'professionals'. The sop to their consciences was the perception that with the ever increasing advances in medicine and health care, 'they' would manage it better.

For many elderly people, especially those with long memories, this was a frightening prospect. Older folk who were no longer able to look after themselves had fared particularly badly. Not a few ended their lives in the Public Assistance Institutions, the old workhouses so feared and dreaded. In 1929 workhouses changed their names and attempts were made to modernise them and brighten up the interiors. Many became active geriatric units with their own medical consultants, but the old character and stigma attached to them remained. Consequently, even 40 years later, it wasn't uncommon for a patient to implore a nurse: "Please don't let them send me there."

Just as there is no greater wonder than assisting new life into the world, so there is no greater privilege than caring for the needs of those at the other end of the spectrum. Sadly, however, death doesn't confine itself to the elderly and there are many occasions when a nurse can find herself confronted with its less acceptable face.

It is inevitable that death has been, and always will be, part of a nurse's experience on the district. However, it comes in many different guises. It can be the older person's friend and the natural conclusion to the life cycle, or the predictable outcome, or unforeseen result of acute or chronic illness, or something more sinister. It is no respecter of age, sex or social status and can sometimes take us completely unawares, striking with cruel suddenness and unbelievable tragedy.

Stillbirth

There are few things more tragic than the loss of a baby during childbirth, or the death of a youngster which evoke such raw emotions. Words are loosely bandied about – 'tragedy', 'waste', 'unnecessary', fall from our lips, and our confidence in the apparent omnipotence of our modern hi-tech Health Service is momentarily shaken. At one time the loss of a child at birth or during childhood was quite commonplace and more readily accepted. Now we no longer expect such catastrophes and are ill-equipped emotionally to deal with them.

During my time on the district I was mercifully spared the trauma of stillbirth, although the post-natal care of those women who had suffered the distress of such an event was very much part of my role as they were always discharged from hospital to home as soon as possible. However, no two people address the situation in the same way.

Throughout her pregnancy the only worry Shirley had was that shared by most women: "Will my baby be normal?" She had never considered for one moment that it might not even be born alive.

"Had he been malformed in any way, I think I could have accepted it better – perhaps with relief even – but he was perfect," she wept.

Every time I visited she went through the agony of questioning: "Why? Why? Why?" The extinguishing of an unspoiled life before it had a chance to begin seemed totally pointless.

Julie, who lost twins within 48 hours of delivery, reacted very differently:

"When I went into premature labour I can remember thinking, quite rationally and coolly, that their chances of survival would be considerably reduced. The staff prepared me for the possibilities but I had already worked it out in my own mind. I had a brief glimpse of two perfectly formed bundles that were my babies, before they were whisked away into incubators. In a peculiar way, I felt quite detached. I've never been a particularly emotional person and perhaps that helped."

Two similar experiences but with completely different reactions, therefore their continuing needs were quite dissimilar. Shirley spent long periods weeping copiously and became quite withdrawn, leaving her devastated husband and parents at a loss to know how best to cope with her. This presented a long-term challenge for me as the midwife. Julie's demands were altogether different, matter-of-fact and modest. In fact, she felt almost guilty that she did not appear to match up to the expectations of a grieving mother.

Both women later went on to give birth to normal, healthy babies who survived boisterously.

Cot Death

The Walkers appeared to be the perfect family: mother, father and two children living comfortably in a modern detached house in the village. They joined in the local activities and were sensible and caring parents. So, when Sally became pregnant for the third time and requested a home confinement I was delighted. The scenario was every midwife's dream.

The pregnancy was uneventful as was the delivery. The husband called me out during a September night and at 5 a.m., just as the fingers of dawn were probing the sky, a beautiful little girl joined an excited brother and sister. The post-natal period was a joy and after the statutory 10 days care I handed the case over to the Health Visitor. Nothing but happy memories remained, coupled with the pleasure I felt on seeing them out and about.

Tuesday afternoons were always devoted to the ante-natal clinic at the surgery which was being conducted by Dr. Rivers and me. We had barely started when the door to the waiting room burst open and a distraught Sally appeared clutching the baby in her arms. Going over to the reception desk she blurted out to a startled Jane: "Please get someone to help, she's not breathing."

Walking out of the consulting rooms I was just in time to hear the anguished cry and quickly shepherded her through to my examination room while Jane urgently summoned the doctor.

Taking the baby in my arms I could feel my heart sinking. She was deathly white, cold and limp. Laying her on the couch I quickly removed the knitted woollen coat and little bonnet and had just pulled up the dress to expose the chest when Dr. Rivers came in. Gravely he listened for a heart beat with his stethoscope and started gentle cardiac massage. Our eyes met and I knew that this was purely for the benefit of the parents who now both stood behind us, desperate for some sign that all would be well.

Sadly, it was not to be. Little Elizabeth had become yet another victim of Sudden Infant Death Syndrome, or Cot Death.

It transpired that Sally had followed the usual routine of bathing the baby that morning, giving her a feed and putting her in her pram in the garden. Her husband arrived home for his lunch and, before returning to work, went to check on his little daughter, only to find her lifeless body. In a vain dash the frantic couple had driven to the surgery. With tears in my eyes I replaced little Elizabeth's clothes and recalled her birth only 10 weeks earlier. This lovely young family were now faced with the long road of grief and bereavement that awaited them.

Cot death is an absolutely devastating occurrence which is made even worse by the required police involvement, as in all cases of sudden unexplained death. Although we went through the motions for the rest of the day, there weren't many dry eyes and none of the surgery staff could fully concentrate, nor would we ever forget a tragic event which had an effect on the whole community.

A Battle Lost

Another such case was that of Holly Evans. I had been asked to visit following her discharge from hospital, where she had suffered the trauma of losing a leg as the result of Ewing's sarcoma.

Holly was 15 years old, one of four children, and lived in a modest terraced house in the village. She was a thin girl, taller than average and a fanatical young sportswoman. When she began complaining of intermittent pain in her right thigh it was initially attributed to sport strain until it increased in intensity and there were signs of localised swelling and tenderness.

Ewing's sarcoma is a malignant tumour, more commonly found in the bones of pelvis or femur, and usually develops in young adolescents when their bones are growing rapidly. The treatment at that time was by means of surgery and radiation. For Holly a straight-forward amputation wasn't possible and the whole leg had to be completely removed by means of disarticulation at the hip.

Mrs. Evans ushered me into their lounge where a single bed had been set up and a wheelchair occupied one corner. Holly was nowhere to be seen.

"She's taken this really badly, Sister. Well, it's been a terrible shock for us all. My husband is particularly devastated and very angry."

I had already learned from Jane that the gentleman concerned had a very short fuse at the best of times. Fortunately, on this occasion, he was at work.

"Where is Holly now?" I asked

"In the other room. I'm afraid she doesn't want to see you because she can't see any point."

Nevertheless, she led me along a narrow hall and I noticed a steep, narrow staircase ascending to the right.

"Sister's here," she announced.

Holly was sitting in a high-backed chair desultorily leafing through a magazine and didn't even look up. One solitary leg was stretched out in front of her and a pair of crutches stood sentinel at the side. She appeared very pale and her straight hair hung lank and lifeless.

Recognising that this wasn't going to be easy I tentatively launched in.

"Holly, I realise that after weeks in hospital the last person you want around is someone else in uniform. I have no intention of staying long, but I do need to carry out an assessment to make sure that you have got everything that it is possible to provide in order to make life manageable for you."

"Unless you've brought me another leg, you're wasting your time," she muttered sulkily.

"Holly," her mother said despairingly, "you know you'll get your artificial leg as soon as the doctors think you're ready."

"Look, supposing I just run through a few things with you so that I can get a better understanding of how things are?"

"If you want," she mumbled indifferently.

"May I sit down?" Taking the shrug of her shoulders as assent, I pulled up a chair.

"Holly, I want you to be totally honest with me, and if you want to shout and scream, feel free. I've got a pretty thick skin and fairly tough eardrums."

Somewhat surprised, she at last looked up.

"Why would I do that?" she asked.

"Well, I think I probably would in your situation."

Sensing that I had her attention, I continued.

"Try to explain to me the things that are frustrating you most at the moment."

"I wouldn't even know where to begin," she almost snarled.

"Just try."

"Well, for a start my bed's downstairs and my bedroom and all my clothes and personal things are upstairs. Can you imagine what it's like having to ask someone to fetch every little thing you want? No, you can't."

As if a dam had been released she continued to give voice.

"I haven't had a bath since I left hospital. Where's the bathroom? Upstairs. You try strip washing in the kitchen or attempt to wash your hair leaning over a sink on one leg."

In an anguished voice her mother interrupted: "Holly, I'm trying to help you as much as I can," she protested.

"I don't want your help. I'm a teenager and I want to do it myself in privacy," she almost screamed.

"OK," I said, "one thing at a time. Let's look at the problem with the stairs. Can you walk on your crutches to the bottom of the staircase, Holly?"

"Of course I can."

"Right, let's do it."

Once gathered at the foot of the stairs, which had a solid rail up either side, I addressed the young girl.

"I'm going to try to pretend that I am you." With my back to the stairs and standing on one leg, I put a hand on each rail and lowered myself onto the second tread. Using only one leg and my hands I hotched up a step at a time on my bottom and reached the top.

"Now," I said, "this is the tricky bit and we will need to get you a spare set of crutches, one for downstairs and one for up."

It wasn't the simplest of manoeuvres but I managed to haul myself upright.

"Coming down will be easier," I said, bumping on my bottom down the stairs.

"Alright, I know I look ridiculous, but where there's a will there's a way. You're younger and more attractive than I am so you should look much better doing it. Will you give it a go?" With much greater agility than I managed, Holly was soon at the top, with me walking close behind her up each step.

"If you decide to attempt this Holly, you certainly mustn't do it unless someone is with you. Do you understand? I know it doesn't give you complete independence but it's still better than what you've got now."

"I promise," she said with something approaching excitement.

"Now, let's look at the bathroom."

This proved to be fairly standard and a quick glance showed that another of Holly's dreams was possible.

"I'm just going out to get something from my car."

Within a couple of minutes I was back clutching a bath board.

"Right, let's go upstairs again and tackle the next hurdle."

Placing the board across the bath, I turned to Holly.

"All you have to do is come in, sit down on the board and prop your crutches between the basin and bath. You can then get undressed and use the basin to hold onto if you need to stand. Then you swing your leg over and into the bath, like this, and using the pressure of your arms lower yourself into the bath, like so."

"You do look funny sitting in the bath fully dressed, Sister," Holly giggled.

"Believe me, my dear, I've looked funny for most of my life," I smiled wryly. "However, it hasn't stopped me from achieving the things I wanted to, so don't knock it. Now you come and have a try."

In a flash the feat was accomplished. Noticing the shower head and hose lying on the bath rack I suggested that she would also be able to wash her hair whilst in the bath.

"How's that?" I enquired.

"Good," she replied with a real smile on her face.

"It's certainly enough for one day but I'll be back to see how you're getting on. Save any other problems till then."

By the time of my next visit, the bed had disappeared from the lounge, the spare pair of crutches was in place and Holly appeared to be less lacklustre.

"Once I get my artificial leg, it'll be a piece of cake," she informed me.

"Right, young lady, what's next on your wish list?"

"I've started back at school for mornings only. A car comes to fetch me and the wheelchair," she said.

"Well, that's another bit of progress, isn't it?"

"I suppose so, but the only thing I've ever really been interested in, or any good at for that matter, is sport. Now that's been taken away along with my leg."

"What sports were you good at, or what did you enjoy most?" I asked.

"Sprinting, high jump and swimming," she replied morosely.

I had already been mulling this matter over in my mind and had made some enquiries. "Holly, you and I both know that sprinting and high jump will be out but there's no reason at all why you can't still swim. You've already demonstrated that you've got considerable power in your arms. There are plenty of amputees competing in disabled swimming championships, so that's very much a possibility. There is a physical training college not too far away with all the necessary facilities."

A glint of interest showed in her face.

"Another sport which I think would suit you is archery."

"Archery?" she said in surprise.

"Why ever not? It requires upper body strength, can be done from a wheelchair and is also competitive."

"Where would I do that?"

"The same place as the swimming. Would you be prepared to give it a try?"

"I'll try anything."

"Right then, there's something else which I think would benefit you, and that is riding for the disabled. Have you ever ridden a horse?"

"Never," she said, positively glowing with excitement.

"The thing about riding is that it will help your balance, so it won't only be a pleasure but beneficial too. Fortunately there is a centre reasonably near. However, none of this is going to be arranged instantly and you'll need clearance from the hospital first. The important thing is that there are still sporting challenges out there for you to take part in and should give you a goal to work towards."

Within a reasonably short time the long-awaited prosthetic leg arrived and Holly embarked upon the road to recovery. There was no need for my continued involvement which would merely serve to remind her that she was a 'patient'. I often saw her out and about with her friends and occasionally heard reports of the strides which she was making, especially with swimming. Thus, Holly was discharged from my caseload and we both moved on.

Only two years later, the news we were praying would never happen, reared its head. She developed a cough, breathlessness and fatigue and tests showed that the cancer had spread to her lungs. It was the worst possible scenario and I steeled myself to return to the house. Once more the bed was back in the living room and we set about acquiring the necessary nursing aids such as a sheepskin, ripple mattress and commode. With her skeletal frame, the last thing she needed was pressure sores. How much Holly ever suspected, or understood, regarding her condition we never knew, nor did she ask. Instead she meekly accepted the twice daily visits from members of the team but the previous spark, whether of anger, sulks or frustration, had gone and she became virtually monosyllabic, as though the effort of holding a conversation was frankly too much.

Mercifully, Holly didn't linger for long. Arriving one morning to carry out the daily general care I rapidly realised that the end was not far off. Summoning the parents to come and hold her hands and talk to her we kept a short vigil. Between us we recalled everything that she had achieved despite an appalling handicap, especially five medals gained in swimming, including two golds, until she peacefully slipped beyond our reach.

Her father who, despite the best endeavours on the part of nurses and doctors, resolutely declined to accept the facts, now refused to acknowledge that Holly had died.

"No! No! No!" he kept saying. "Do something Sister." Finally, he got up from his position by the bed and sped from the room wailing like a banshee.

Torn between concern for him and the grieving figure of his weeping wife, she simply said: "Leave him, Sister, it's his way. I'll go to him later."

As I set about removing as much nursing gear as possible from the room, which would only serve as a constant reminder of a battle lost, Mr. Evans reappeared. Picking up the artificial leg which had been propped in a corner, he almost threw it at me.

"Here, take this bloody thing. I never want to set eyes on it again."

I drove straight home, flung the offending limb into the back of the garage and went indoors and sobbed.

It was the day before my birthday.

A Pointless Waste

Joan Wyndham was in her early fifties and first came to my attention early in 1976 following her discharge from hospital, where she had been treated for bronchopneumonia. The discharge letter merely requested follow-up assessment and check visits by the district nurse as necessary.

Had it not been for the local knowledge of our inestimable receptionists I would have remained ignorant as to what awaited me, for the information omitted one salient sentence: 'This patient is an alcoholic of long standing.'

Jane and Edna had known Joan from their teens. According to their account she was an exceedingly attractive girl and had won local beauty contests. They all went to dances together and she was never short of young admirers. Joan, however, had other ideas and set her sights on an older man who was a successful farmer and quite comfortably off. His parents had died and left him the farm and a beautiful, if rather isolated, old house in pleasant gardens. Clive Wyndham was completely infatuated by her and, within a fairly short space of time, they were married. His quietness was the perfect foil for her vivacity.

Nothing was too good for Joan and her every whim was catered for. She was given free rein to reorganise the décor of the home; a swimming pool appeared followed by a tennis court and there were many parties and much entertaining where the drinks flowed freely. To the delight of her husband she dutifully produced a boy and a girl, and they appeared to have everything. But Joan was never satisfied and could spend money like water. Things reached a pitch where the farm had to be remortgaged and Clive, whose hair had become prematurely snow white, was fighting a constant battle to keep afloat. Any visitors began to realise that Joan's social drinking had become her prop and stay.

"It's absolutely pathetic to see her now," Jane said. "Her figure and her looks have gone, she doesn't seem to bother with her appearance and her manner is quite brittle."

"Who else lives there?" I enquired.

"There's only her and Clive. The children left home as soon as possible and are now working in London, I think. I haven't seen them for ages."

I followed the lane leading out of the village toward the marshes. Dykes ran parallel on either side and I made a mental note to avoid it in the fog if at all possible. After many twists and turns I spotted the ivy-covered walls of a substantial brick house in the distance. It stood well back from the road and was accessed by a drive which had clearly been tarmac at some time, but was now a broken uneven surface deeply invaded by weeds. The flower borders on either side were overgrown, but the adjacent fields seemed well cultivated and looked quite healthy. At the top of the drive was a swimming pool which now lay empty, the tiles cracked and weeds growing everywhere. Beyond the pool was a tennis court in a similar neglected state. The lawn had been cut but the herbaceous borders were untended. The whole scene was that of a property whose occupants had long since given up.

As I got out of the car a man emerged from the back door.

"Mr. Wyndham?" I enquired.

A slight, welcoming smile lit up the face of a tired-looking man in his late sixties who had a head of the whitest hair imaginable.

"That's right, Sister. I guess you've come to see my wife?"

"I'm just calling to see how she is and to make sure that you can manage."

"We're alright," he said in a voice so quiet I could scarcely hear him. "We'll cope."

"May I go in and see your wife?"

"Please do, though I don't think you'll get much of a welcome. She just wants to be left alone," he replied.

"Well, I'll just check. She may not want to see me, but if at any time you think I can help, please phone the surgery and I'll come out. All right?"

"Thank you Sister, we will. Use the back door, just walk in. She'll either be in the living room or upstairs in her bedroom."

With that he walked off slowly down the drive.

Joan was hunched in a corner of the sofa, a glass in one hand and a cigarette in the other. Her nightdress was covered with a silk dressing gown of faded peach that had seen better days and her feet were drawn up beneath her. She was extremely thin, her skin had the appearance of cream parchment and her hair was sparse, dry and almost orange. Had I not been told her age I would have been unable to guess.

"Come to spy on me have you, Sister?" The voice was hard and accusing.

"On the contrary, Mrs. Wyndham, I'm only here to see that you have everything you need and to ask whether you require any help at all?"

"Help with what?"

"Well, what about washing, bathing and dressing?"

"I'll wash when I want to and if I choose to lounge around all day in my night clothes, that's my business. My husband can help with anything I need."

"Are you able to get something to eat?"

186

"I probably could if I wished to but I'm not hungry. I may have something when Clive comes in this evening."

Casting my eye over a room which was clean and tidy, but faded and unloved, I smiled at her and said: "You've got a beautiful house here but it must make a lot of work for you?"

"A woman comes in and cleans through. There's not much to do with just the two of us."

"What about family?"

"We've got two children but they work away. My daughter is coming down at the weekend and she'll sort everything."

"Mrs. Wyndham, I'm not going to keep hustling you but you've had a nasty chest infection and you are inevitably a bit weak. If you don't mind, I'll pop in from time to time when I'm passing but if you need our help in the meantime you only have to ask."

To this she agreed. I left far from happy but there was nothing to be gained by alienating her at the first visit by persisting further.

Similar visits over the next month were equally fruitless and there were never any signs of the husband or anyone else. However, it was quite clear that her general condition was far from satisfactory. Following a phone call from Clive saying that he could no longer cope, and a visit from Dr. Chase, she was re-admitted to hospital, this time with hepatic failure.

In June the staff decided that Joan should come home for a trial weekend but didn't consider it necessary for the district nurses to visit. By chance I saw Clive standing by his car in the High Street of my home village on the Friday afternoon.

"I've just been to fetch Joan," he said. "She wanted to get a few things from the shop," indicating the local store.

"If at any time you feel it getting on top of you, just pick up the phone and I'll come."

"Thank you but I'm sure we'll last till Monday. The daughter's coming tomorrow."

Two trial weekends at home took place before the hospital decided to discharge her permanently on a Friday afternoon. Unfortunately they failed to inform the surgery until eleven o'clock on the following Monday morning. By the time the discharge letter arrived in the post, however, it was too late and Clive had phoned the surgery to say that he could no longer manage the situation and would a nurse please visit as soon as possible. The letter contained a lengthy list of medication and a request for care when required, as the doctors considered there was nothing else that they could do. Her liver was packing up and the patient was in a terminal state.

Having just come to the end of my surgery session I left immediately for the farm. At the approach to the drive I spotted Clive on his tractor, apparently crop-spraying. We both waved in acknowledgement and I proceeded to the house, entering by the back door as usual. There was no sign of Joan downstairs so I went up to her bedroom. To my complete and utter horror I found her lying on the bed with an upturned, yellow plastic bowl on her chest. Vomit had spilled everywhere and the bedding was soaked with urine. Examination showed that Joan was very clearly dead. I could not believe what I was seeing.

Dashing to the phone I managed to contact Dr. Chase, who was fortunately still at the surgery, and was relieved to hear him say: "Don't worry, I'll be there directly."

As I replaced the receiver, Clive came in through the back door. Taking his boots off he padded through into the hall saying in his usual quiet voice: "I thought I'd better come in case you need some help. We've had an awful time with her."

"Come into the lounge for a moment," I said, "and let's both sit down."

As gently as I could I broke the news to him. If I was expecting some dramatic reaction, it certainly wasn't forthcoming. On the few occasions on which we had met I had always found him very quiet, and there appeared something vague and ineffective about him. Now he sat on the settee, with head downcast, twiddling his hands together between his knees.

"Can you bear to tell me what happened over the weekend," I probed.

In a subdued tone, he replied: "The hospital discharged her on Friday and said there was nothing more to be done and that she was getting near the end. My son and daughter came down immediately but we soon found it impossible to handle her."

Looking up he sighed before continuing.

"The rapport between them all has never been particularly good Sister, and they really had very little contact with their mother. I suppose they found it too painful."

"Where are they now?" I asked.

"They've gone back to London. You see, as the weekend progressed, my wife became more and more demanding, disgruntled, aggressive and difficult to manage, to the extent that any attempts to attend to her bodily needs were eventually abandoned."

"Why on earth didn't you phone for help?" I found it quite difficult to conceal my exasperation. "We didn't even know Joan had been discharged until this morning."

"We thought we'd be able to cope for a bit longer," he said helplessly. "Then my daughter rang the hospital yesterday and spoke to the doctor to ask how long he thought her mother had left, and whether he considered she should apply for compassionate leave because she seemed worse."

"What did he say?"

"Simply that although her condition was terminal, her death was by no means imminent."

He paused for a moment before saying: "Quite frankly, I didn't consider her state to be greatly different than it has been on numerous occasions over the past three months."

"For goodness sake, you should have asked for help," I sighed.

"Joan wouldn't have it and, quite frankly, you wouldn't have been able to handle her any more than we could," he explained morosely. "The children were ashamed of her, too. After they'd spoken to the hospital and learned that this could go on for quite a while, they had no choice but to return to London."

"So, what happened last night?"

Wearily he said: "Joan had me up every half hour throughout the night until, I'll be honest with you, I came to the end of my tether. So I got up early and went out to lose myself on the farm."

Looking up, he added hastily: "I came back at breakfast time to give her a drink and her tablets."

"How was she then?"

"Actually she was a bit incoherent, but she swallowed them and I went out again. I returned about half an hour before you arrived. I crept upstairs and saw from the landing that she seemed to be sleeping so went back to the fields."

I thought for a moment before asking, "When you observed her from the landing, was there a yellow plastic bowl on her chest?"

"Where it was I couldn't exactly say but she'd always got it close to hand, Sister. She was forever feeling sick."

Dr. Chase arrived and between us we tried to make Joan a little more presentable while Clive telephoned the children.

It was quite hopeless to detect what emotions this man was feeling and impossible to really get alongside him. This was not a case that any of us could look back on with fondness or pride for it was one of abysmal failure and poor communication. However, I do not think that any more aggressive intervention on the part of the community staff would have prevented the final outcome of this pitiful story. At most perhaps it would have been accomplished in a less traumatic fashion.

It is the unassailable right of every human being to die with as much dignity, comfort and care as it is possible to give and I was upset and appalled by the manner of Joan's death.

Addiction of any kind is a terrible thing, not only for the individual concerned but all who have to live with them. Here was a woman with everything in the world to live for who had, with complete selfishness and lack of consideration for her family, pushed the self-destruct button.

Sadly, there are some people who actually won't be helped. As her daughter said when I eventually met her two days later: "You can take a horse to water but you can't make it drink it. Water was certainly the last thing my mother ever considered."

Peace At The Last

When King Charles II lay on his death bed he is alleged to have said to the retinue of courtiers standing around: "I am sorry gentlemen, for being such a long while dying." Indeed, on occasion death can seem to be an inordinately lengthy business.

Sadie Green was approaching 90 and, some time previously, had moved from her little cottage to be cared for by her son and daughter-in-law. The day came when Maisie couldn't get her up and dressed as she usually did every morning. Visited by the doctor they were advised that the old lady's body was slowly giving up and she just needed to be left in peace and comfort.

"I'll ask the district nurses to come," he said; an offer which they were only too ready to accept.

When I arrived, Sadie was lying on a high, iron double bedstead in the sitting room. As much furniture as possible had been removed, but even so space remained extremely cramped and it was only just possible to walk round the vast bed. Everything was quite dated but very clean and the attendant Maisie was clearly anxious to do as much as she could to help.

"She's been such a dear," she confided. "The best mother-in-law anyone could have had."

Between us things were set in place. The nurses visited morning and evening and Maisie was shown how to keep the mouth moistened, the lips greased to prevent dryness and cracking, and to offer sips of liquid which was all the nourishment the drowsy Sadie could be persuaded to take. Although she was aware of our presence there was no attempt to communicate beyond the occasional smile and a weak squeeze of the hand. Here was a soul who was simply worn out and whose life was drawing to its natural close.

Each time we visited I congratulated Maisie on how well she was doing.

"How long is it likely to be Sister, because it doesn't seem right that the rest of us are eating and talking next door as if nothing is happening?"

"We've even got the 'telly' on low and there's the odd laugh," her husband confessed.

"And why ever should you not?" I said. "If she is aware of them, which I doubt, these are sounds which will all be familiar and comforting to your mother. As for length of time I'm afraid I can't presume to say. The important thing is that she is warm and comfortable and isn't in any pain. In fact, you are probably suffering more than she is."

"Too right," replied her son with a grimace.

Little did any of us realise that this situation would continue for another week. Eventually, on a Sunday evening, when I arrived to give the usual care and settle her for the night, I realised that the end was imminent. Sadie was evidencing Cheyne-Stokes respiration which is an abnormal pattern of breathing often seen before a death. It is characterised by deep sometimes faster breathing, followed by a gradual decrease that results in a temporary pause until it finishes completely.

Approaching the family I suggested that they might like to come and sit with her. They gathered awkwardly round the bed to say their goodbyes, but professed themselves unable to remain there. Therefore, it was left to me to keep company with Sadie till she breathed her last.

By this time it was eight o'clock and if a patient dies whilst a nurse is with them she is expected to stay and perform the last offices. I had recently re-married and, realising that I would be very

191

late home, I rang my husband to explain. Meanwhile, Maisie and her husband were sitting in a state of some bemusement when I suggested that they might like to contact the undertaker.

"We couldn't, Sister. Will you sort it for us?"

Finally, at 9.30 p.m., our friendly funeral director arrived with one of his assistants.

After speaking to the family, who remained resolutely closeted together in the back room, I led him into the bedroom.

"Goodness Sister, this is a bit tight for space," he commented.

"Yes, it isn't going to be the easiest of exercises, especially as she's also floundering in the ubiquitous feather mattress. I think you'll need me to give you a hand."

With everything at last in place we prepared to move Sadie.

"If we stand at either end and you kneel on the bed in the middle, Sister, that would be helpful," he said.

The assistant wasn't exactly the sharpest knife in the drawer, but he had been given employment by a very sympathetic man who patiently nurtured him along. Both men were keen bell-ringers at the local church which they attended. I had already placed my hands underneath to support Sadie's body when, to my astonishment, the lad remarked out of nowhere: "We've been to church this evening."

"Alright Peter, let's just concentrate on what we're doing shall we?" his boss said.

"Yes, but do you remember who we prayed for?" he asked in his expressionless tone.

By now I was totally bemused and not a little uncomfortable in my somewhat awkward position. Looking helplessly at the undertaker I heard the voice continue:

"We prayed for nurses and I wouldn't have done if I'd known what this one had got up her sleeve!"

Trying very hard to control our amusement the lift was accomplished, Sadie was finally borne away, and I could seek the comfort of my home.

However, another surprise awaited me. My husband welcomed me back saying: "You must be shattered. Can I get you something?"

"Yes," I replied, gratefully sinking into the armchair. "I'd like a Whisky Mac and a cigarette."

Returning with the drink, he queried what I had been doing that took so long.

"Well, I'm afraid my patient died whist I was there so I had to lay her out and wait for the undertakers," I informed him matter-of-factly.

My husband's acquaintance with all things nursing and medical had, until our recent marriage, been absolutely non-existent. Eying me somewhat askance he firmly held on to the drink saying: "Don't you think you should go and have a bath first?

Regarding him with some surprise, I said: "I will when I've had a drink. What's the hurry?"

"Well you've been handling a dead body."

I stopped short in amazement. I suppose that death was so much part of my work that I had never stopped to think how other people might view it. Despite my meticulous ablutions I was aware that my husband kept very much to his own side of the bed that night.

Thankfully, he rapidly became immune!

Terminal Illnesses

Defining terminal illness with regard to the length of time remaining is not an easy matter. The term was popularised in the 20th century to describe a disease that cannot be cured or adequately treated and is reasonably expected to result in the death of the patient within a short period of time – often six months or less.

Inevitably doctors and nurses are frequently asked the question: "How long has he, or she, got?" If the answer to that was known life would be much simpler for everyone. It is generally unwise to provide estimates for fear of instilling false hopes. There are those who may gear themselves to meet a six month deadline and will feel cheated if their loved one fails to survive for that length of time. Similarly, they can find themselves running out of steam, both physically and emotionally, the longer the time frame is extended.

Billy Southall was in his mid-twenties, the only child of older parents who ran a family business which he was being groomed to take over at a later stage. He first came to my attention in 1974 when his father developed bowel cancer. Surgical intervention proved unsuccessful and this capable yet quiet, unassuming man died within nine months. Billy was devastated, but determined to carry on as usual with the help of a manager until he was able to assume the reins completely.

Fate, however, had other ideas and gave the lie to the saying that lightning doesn't strike twice in the same place. Only two years later

Billy was also diagnosed with the same cancer that had so recently killed his father. Once again surgery failed and this young man returned home, pale, gaunt and skeletally thin.

At the time of his discharge, the hospital, GP and nurses were all convinced that his remaining life expectancy would be of extremely short duration. A hospital bed and a hoist were procured and the lounge converted to meet his needs.

So began one of the most harrowing nursing experiences any of us had known. Billy had absolutely no strength to undertake even the simplest task, such as holding a cup unaided. His mother was quietly distraught and, although she was a constant hovering presence, never felt that she could undertake much in the way of actual physical care. It was a constant fight to prevent bedsores breaking out on his emaciated body and pain very soon began to evince itself. Although he never once complained, the cries emitted each time he was moved and the anguished look on his face told their own story. A urinary catheter was inserted for his comfort and ease of management.

Double-handed care was needed twice a day and morphine injections were administered at eight in the morning, four in the afternoon and ten at night. The nurses weren't obliged to undertake late evening visits but, in the absence of any out-of-hours service, many did so in order to ensure the best possible pain control in difficult circumstances. In this we were often supported by the doctors who would also take a turn to do the late call.

With the advent of the Syringe Driver in the early '80s, this aspect of care was to revolutionise the situation for patient and carers. A Syringe Driver is a small, portable, battery-driven infusion pump used to give medicines subcutaneously via a syringe, usually over a period of 24 hours. The most popular use was in palliative care, to continuously administer drugs to ensure pain relief and control nausea and vomiting and other unpleasant side effects which the patient may experience. The obvious benefit of this was the prevention of medication levels becoming too high or too low, and avoided the use of multiple tablets and injections.

Unfortunately, this wasn't available to us when caring for Billy. Very popular in end-of-life care at this time, however, was an elixir taken by mouth called Brompton Cocktail. It contained morphine or heroin, cocaine, chlorpromazine, honey and alcohol of the patient's choice of gin, brandy or whisky. This was virtually all that was on offer beside injections of morphine or heroin. Only a few years later this mixture fell into disuse, as the hospice movement developed improved methods of palliative care.

The days turned into weeks and the weeks became a month, but still Billy clung tenuously to life. Due to take a week's annual leave I hoped that I would be able to draw a line under this unhappy state of affairs before my departure, but it wasn't to be. Bidding him 'goodbye' I confidently thought it would be our last contact.

When my colleague phoned to hand back my caseload the following Sunday evening, I could barely contain myself.

"When did Billy die?" I asked urgently. There was a pause before the reply came.

"Ann, you're not going to believe it but he's still with us."

Incredulously, I made my way to his home first thing the following morning. The sight awaiting me was pathetic. Now strongly resembling an inmate in an infamous concentration camp, Billy could only manage to communicate in a hoarse whisper while his tortured eyes seemed hauntingly fixed on whoever was ministering to him. To my dismay the condition of his skin was now such that he had developed a small sore behind one ear where the surface had rested on the pillow.

Feeling thoroughly frustrated, powerless and incensed I left the house and proceeded to drive like a bat out of hell along the lanes to the surgery. Fortuitously, I spotted Dr. Chase's car coming towards me and I flashed my lights, sounded the horn and slammed on the brakes. Jumping out I confronted him saying angrily: "This situation with Billy really can't go on and 'Someone Up There' clearly isn't listening to a word I'm saying."

Possibly sensing that the top of the volcano was about to blow, he replied sympathetically: "I know, but you obviously haven't heard the latest news."

The steam immediately went out of me and, descending to earth with a bump, I anxiously enquired what had happened. Fixing me with a hint of a twinkle in his eye, he replied: "God's decided to go on holiday for a fortnight."

Those words were sufficient to defuse the tension that had been building up inside me and I grimaced apologetically. It is almost inevitable that there will be occasions when nurses become emotionally involved with patients, but it is always necessary to maintain a sense of proportion and control.

"Don't worry Ann, I'm as concerned as you are and I'm on my

way there now to see what else, if anything, I can possibly do." Not for the first time I realised how fortunate all the team members were to be able to enjoy such mutual support and rapport.

Two weeks before my holiday I had applied for the help of a Marie Curie nurse for Billy. The Marie Curie Nursing Service was established in 1948. It is a charitable organisation which provides free one-to-one overnight care from a registered nurse, usually for eight to nine hours, for patients dying at home from end-stage cancer. This facility was a lifeline for both hard-pressed families and district nurses. However, their resources were finite and we were limited in the number of nights available to a patient. As the ability to predict the terminality of a disease is not an exact science, it became something of an art to introduce this service at the precise moment when it would be of optimum benefit. I had clearly, though not unreasonably, misjudged the situation by calling them in too early, and we over-ran the time allowed. Mercifully when presented with the scenario the district nurses were faced with, they agreed to accept my colleague's request for extended visits.

It was whilst in the excellent care of the Marie Curie nurse that Billy finally departed this life, two days after my holiday. His poor mother chose to think that he had actually been waiting for me to return. If I had believed in that likelihood I would never have gone away in the first place.

Billy proved to be the catalyst that made me determined to pursue every means possible to improve the care available for cancer patients in the community. The opportunity came the following year when I was sent on a Study Day for Nurses at St. Christopher's Hospice in Sydenham. I came away elated and fired with enthusiasm, for I had glimpsed an ideal and briefly tasted the cream in care of the terminally ill. Yet my prime emotions were frustration and anger that this philosophy of care was not available to my patients.

Hospices were few and far between at that time and symptom-control for cancer patients in the community was fairly hit-and-miss, and heavily dependent on the prescribing skills of the individual doctor. Advances in this sphere of medicine were revolutionising existence for this group of people, providing an improved quality of life physically and emotionally, not only for the sufferer but for the whole family too. I had been privileged to see just what could be achieved but, in order to experience such care, it was necessary to live in the right catchment area. The south-east corner of England was not only lacking a hospice — it couldn't even boast an evening nursing service in the community, let alone a night service.

I returned to my normal daily round on the district, but that niggling dissatisfaction in my mind wouldn't go away. The hospice ethos was constantly creeping into my conversations until I could think and speak of nothing else. Encouraged by the interested reactions of others, I decided to try and bring a group of people together to explore whether it would be possible to raise sufficient money to build a hospice in the area. To my relief the decision was taken to embark upon such an enterprise.

Ann discusses plans for the new hospice in her role as chairman

So began a manic four years, juggling the demands of an everyday working life with those of evangelising and fundraising for the hospice and also my Chairmanship of the project. Very few people even knew what a hospice was and it became vital to seize every opportunity to inform and publicise our goal. I gradually found myself with a diary fully committed to speaking engagements in the evenings, plus a rapidly increasing knowledge of the geography of East Kent.

Arriving home at lunchtime on a wet and dreary January day, I was just in time to receive a call from the local television station. A male voice at the end of the phone requested my presence for an interview on Scene South East Television following the six o'clock news. My first reaction was totally irrelevant but typically female – "What shall I wear?"

"Oh, just come as you are," said the disembodied voice.

I surveyed my dripping raincoat and mud-spattered boots, glanced at my watch, mentally reviewed the nursing visits still to be made and wished fervently that television presenters had heard of forward planning.

It eventually became clear that something would have to go if this pace was to be maintained. Supportive colleagues covered for me if the occasion arose, but getting up in the night for the occasional maternity cases was draining. The time had come to completely relinquish midwifery and I finally delivered my last baby in 1980. Mercifully I was too busy to suffer from withdrawal symptoms.

Meanwhile, the number of patients who would have benefited from hospice care continued to increase. Cancer became the 'Big C' in people's minds but it wasn't the only gremlin to be addressed.

John Baker was a young man of 35 when he was referred by the hospital into the care of the district nurses. Some years previously he had been identified as having polyneuritis, a term that refers to inflammation or damage to nerves, usually affecting the feet and legs. Common symptoms are tingling sensations, pins and needles and episodes of numbness.

Time proved the initial diagnosis to be wrong as the disease progressed into what was thought to be multiple sclerosis. This is an inflammatory condition in which the fatty myelin sheaths around the brain and spinal cord are damaged, creating the formation of scars or plaques which cause physical problems varying according to which area has been affected. This disorder often progresses to physical and cognitive restriction, dependent on the form it takes, becoming either acutely progressive or relapsing and remitting. John appeared to cope well by using a specially controlled car and with the aid of crutches or a wheelchair, depending on the severity of his disability at any given time.

I had first met John when attending his wife for post-natal care following the delivery of twins, who were now two-year-old toddlers. They also had a very active little girl of four, so Melanie had her hands full, especially as John became more and more dependent on her for help. Despite this they very rarely troubled the surgery, as he was regularly monitored by the hospital consultant.

However, in 1979 he had the misfortune to fracture his femur

198

following a fall and was admitted to hospital to have it pinned and plated. This episode merely served to exacerbate his general condition and rendered him quadriplegic, with facial palsy and difficulty in swallowing. The original diagnosis of multiple sclerosis was changed to that of motor neurone disease.

In mid-November he was discharged home to the care of his wife. Liaison between hospital and community was notoriously poor at that time. Computers, fax-machines and email were all things of the future and discharge letters invariably took a week to reach the surgery. Pre-planned patient transfer involving physiotherapists, occupational therapists and community staff didn't exist although, normally, we did at least receive a telephone call alerting us regarding specific requests or any likely problems. Unfortunately, for some unfathomable reason, neither the doctors nor district nurses were informed of the situation. It wasn't until a week later, when Mel phoned the surgery first thing on a Monday morning desperate for help, that we became aware of the plight of this family. By good fortune the team happened to be on hand when the call came through and by nine o'clock I was at their home, accompanied by Theresa the Enrolled Nurse.

On arrival we discovered chaos to be reigning supreme. John, partially dressed, was lying on a mattress on the floor whilst his wife struggled to cope with three half-clad toddlers. Mel was a fiercely independent, unflappable and determined lass and had clearly coped admirably above and beyond what could reasonably be expected of any relative. She may well have given the hospital staff the impression that she would be able to manage. Nevertheless, this did not alter the fact that their common intelligence should have told them that a patient who required at least two nurses to move him from chair to bed on a ward, could hardly be dealt with single handedly by a wife with three small children in tow.

Theresa and I managed to lift John from floor to wheelchair with considerable difficulty and couldn't imagine how Mel had coped on her own for a week. Between us we washed, shaved, dressed and settled him comfortably.

I then turned my attention to assessing the home for the provision of possible aids. It was a lovely old cottage, small but quaint, and totally unsuitable for the nursing of this heavily disabled and dependent patient. However, we had to work within the circumstances which presented and, in order to succeed, it would take the co-operation and input of every member of the Primary Health Care Team.

The whole day was taken up trying to address the problem and establish some sort of order. By teatime a hospital profiling bed had been located, delivered and erected in the downstairs study. A Buxton rise and recline chair was obtained along with a replacement wheelchair, as the antediluvian model which John had been using was hideously cumbersome and the brakes didn't work. A sheepskin was obtained and Mel instructed on how to care for the pressure areas which were beginning to show signs of redness.

Ideally, I would have liked to install a hoist, in order to take the strain of lifting, but there was absolutely no room to accommodate this bulky piece of equipment. It was small wonder that so many nurses suffered with back problems at that time. Manual handling training programmes were in their infancy and Health and Safety unheard of.

The Health Visitor was contacted and she managed to arrange play group placements for all three children every morning. Meanwhile, the helpful local vicar's wife arrived and removed the children to spend the rest of the day and one night with her own offspring, in order to give Mel a much needed break. The Home-Help organiser was also consulted and instituted an emergency service with immediate effect.

The hospital was notified and both doctors and nurses were told by Dr. Chase and myself exactly what we thought about their handling of the discharge. As a result they offered to accept John for hydrotherapy sessions five mornings a week, and the assurance was given of immediate readmission should the situation get out of control.

Arrangements were made for two district nurses to visit at eight o'clock every morning to give general care and prepare him for hospital, to which he would be driven by a friend. However, this still left a gaping void at the end of the day as there was no evening nursing service at that time.

By teatime, although things were still far from satisfactory, I felt that much had been achieved in eight hours to make the situation more tenable.

Nevertheless, several lessons were learned and driven home, not least the need for better liaison between hospital and community. If this had been forthcoming adequate provisions could have been made before discharge home, which is infinitely preferable to walking into a crisis situation.

Once the initial predicament had been resolved I turned my attention to addressing other problems. John was a highly intelligent man and the condition in which he now found himself was making him irritable and frustrated. Thus I set about investigating the possibility of obtaining POSSUM equipment which would help him to maintain some control of his business life and relieve the boredom. People with disability often depend on others for help with activities which the rest of us take for granted, like opening windows, switching on the television and answering the door and telephone. Modern technology enables the carrying out of these tasks and even gives them a voice by providing synthesised speech or text. However, this wasn't going to materialise overnight.

Despite all that we could provide the effect of John's condition on Mel was near intolerable. Not for her the luxury of an undisturbed night. John was unable to change his position unaided, scratch an itch, blow his nose or help himself to a drink if required. Between the needs of her husband and the little ones she was getting up at least eight times. Desperate to provide some extra help, I approached Jane, our surgery receptionist, and between us we recruited a few kindly lay people, known to us, who were prepared to sit with John at night in order to give his wife a rest. However, this could not go on indefinitely.

On the committee of the proposed hospice project was David, a young, enthusiastic social worker, and I approached him to see whether Social Services could offer any input. However, there was nothing available. I explained what the local volunteers had been doing and this sparked a possibility in our minds. Over the ensuing weeks we both watched with keen interest as this small band of ordinary people, with no practical training, had learnt from Mel how to undertake the little tasks needed to ensure John's comfort during the night hours, thereby allowing her to get some much needed sleep.

As a result of this chance experience we decided to try to provide voluntary sitters for terminal cancer patients in their homes. It would certainly enable us to offer a useful, practical facility, long before the doors of the hospice could ever open. It was necessary, however, to be able to satisfy certain criteria in order to be credible and officially recognised. David and I met representatives from the local health authorities, including nursing and social work personnel, and outlined our proposals. We would recruit volunteers and run training courses in the major towns in order to equip them with sufficient knowledge and expertise to allow them to relieve hard-pressed relatives. They would not be expected to perform tasks requiring skilled nursing, purely those undertaken by any caring family member.

The idea was received with reserved enthusiasm but, nonetheless, permission was granted to set the wheels in motion to achieve our aims. Offers came in from District Nurses across the South-East prepared to run training classes in their spare time. The local press did us proud by publicising the exercise in a four-page spread. In four months sufficient people, many of them recently retired nurses, had come forward and four training courses were completed. Within a week the first request for help was received. This marked the establishment of a voluntary night and day sitting service which remained active for years and usefully filled a gap in unmet need at that time. It was yet another example of community spirit in action.

Volunteers for the sitting service are instructed to look after patients by a District Nursing Sister

Sadly, John did not live to witness the success of a scheme which had been spawned from the tragic circumstances surrounding him and his little family. His condition deteriorated remorselessly until increasing problems with swallowing and breathing made admission to hospital inevitable. He died shortly afterwards. Cases like those of Billy and John were only too common amongst District Nurses at that time and we frankly couldn't wait for the day when hospice facilities would be available in the area.

Far exceeding my wildest hopes and expectations, on 8 June 1982 I found myself greeting a smiling Queen Elizabeth the Queen Mother to escort her round the Pilgrims Hospice in Canterbury, which she had graciously agreed to open.

Right: Her Royal Highness, Queen Elizabeth the Queen Mother, meets nursing staff, and below, presents Ann with a signed photograph for the Hospice

ROYAL VISIT TO HOSPICE

203

The person who couldn't wait to hear all the details was, of course, my oldest patient on the district, Edith Wall, now 98. Studying the press photos she said: "Well, we've both seen her Sister, and now you've actually spoken to her and shaken her hand. Neither of us could have imagined that when we mentioned her while talking in this very room all those years ago."

It was the culmination of a remarkable four years and changed the face of palliative care throughout the area.*

While we have little or no control over the diseases that fate has in store, the majority would probably like to feel that they could be in some command regarding the manner of their demise. It is reasonably safe to say that most people, if given the choice, would opt to die in their own home. District Nurses were regularly confronted with the patient who 'refused to budge' no matter what the circumstances.

"The only way they'll get me out of here is feet first in a box Sister," was the reaction of many of my patients over the years. And why should this not be? What better than to meet death within the familiar four walls of your home, surrounded by the well-loved paraphernalia of life and in the company of friends and family? It is certainly cheaper than hospitalisation.

Unfortunately, society as a whole has a somewhat blinkered view. It would prefer death not to happen at all but, if it has to be, then institutions are expected to provide the necessary care. The nuclear family cannot seem to accept death as the extended family did in days gone by. This desire to hospitalise the dying patient can be due to an inability to watch suffering, or a fantasy that hospital will manage to bring about a last-minute cure, or offer superior care.

Some of us can recall the days when the family doctor was unafraid to 'help a patient over the final hurdle'. Indeed, it was tacitly accepted that this was expected without any words being said.

Now, instead of allowing people to peacefully succumb to the end that sooner or later awaits us all, they are all too often subjected to aggressive attempts to keep them alive at any cost. This may be as a result of pressure from families or from fear of litigation, but is often regardless of the quality of life which the sufferer may face.

The full story of *The Pilgrims Hospices in East Kent* by Ann Robertson, 2007, is sold in aid of the Pilgrims Hospices.
Contact: *www.pilgrimshospice.org*

Advances in technology have now made it possible to keep people alive almost indefinitely, not necessarily because we should do so but because we can, thereby rendering them unfortunate victims and prisoners of our modern expertise.

As a result, yet another factor is added to the escalating costs to both state and family at a time when life expectancy is already rising and there are insufficient personnel to care and meet the need. We no longer have a National Health Service but a 'National Keep Death at Bay Service'.

Ironically, this has coincided with an increasing clamour to legalise assisted dying and several high-profile situations have generated much public sympathy. Living wills have come into existence and attempts are being made to give people a greater choice regarding the place and manner of their care at the close of life. Alongside these developments the ever-persistent voice of the euthanasia lobby can also be heard.

It would appear that whilst some doctors and specialists in palliative medicine are trying to manage end-life care sensitively, effectively and with dignity, others are determined to extend life for as long as possible, whilst yet another group apparently can't wait to shuffle off this mortal coil at their own behest.

Dying really has become a very complicated, contrary and controversial business.

Chapter Nine. Coping With Bereavement

 We are all going to die. That is the only certain, inevitable fact in our lives yet I find it astonishing that although we spend nine months preparing for the birth of a child, few if any, spare a thought for the final curtain. Even when there is time to sit back and consider the important things in life, we rarely talk about death, even though sooner or later it catches up with all of us.

Shakespeare said: "All the world's a stage and all men and women merely players. They have their exits and entrances. The acts are seven ages. Last scene of all, that ends this strange eventful history, is second childishness and mere oblivion – sans teeth, sans eyes, sans taste, sans everything."

Death, however, assumes many guises and is an intensely personal event for each individual and family. Unfortunately, despite our many qualifications, members of the health care professions devote so much of our study, time and efforts towards the mastery of modern technological advances and complicated practical procedures, that when it comes to a natural process such as dying, and all that is involved, we are often woefully incompetent. Unless we change our reluctance to talk about dying and plan for the future, we are unlikely to be able to die as we would want with dignity, or to support the dying and bereaved. Every minute someone dies in the UK, but death is all too often shut away, often on a hospital ward or within a care home rather than at home or in a familiar place. By keeping death out of sight and perhaps conveniently out of mind, we have developed a culture that is increasingly lost for words when trying to cope with death and bereavement.

In 1978 I was fortunate enough to be awarded the first Primary Health Care Nursing Award, sponsored by Smith and Nephew Ltd in conjunction with the Royal College of Nursing. My employing authority granted me a three month sabbatical to undertake a tour of the British Isles to assess exactly how the problems of dying, grief and bereavement were being handled in the community, hospitals and other institutions, in order to see what lessons could be learned.

A PRIMARY health care award, exclusively for nursing members of the primary health care team, has been won by Mrs Ann Clayden, a district nurse and midwife, for her essay entitled 'The reality of the primary health care team.'

She is pictured here with Peter Draycon, director of Smith & Nephew Ltd., who sponsored the competition, and organised it in conjunction with the Rcn.

Mrs Clayden intends to use her £1 000 prize money to make a study tour in the United Kingdom to evaluate the methods of caring for terminally ill patients in the community.

Left: Ann receives the award from representatives of Smith & Nephew Ltd.
Below: presenting the results of her findings

I was hugely encouraged by the interest shown in my efforts by doctors, nurses, clergy and Forces chaplains, undertakers, police and Samaritans to name but a few.

More importantly, I was afforded the opportunity to meet with a number of bereaved people in order to understand things from their perspective and to learn from them how we might improve in our handling of this sensitive area.

When I stood on the platform in London to receive the award my predominant emotions were elation, excitement and gratitude. Three months, and 4,000 miles later, with a briefcase full of scribbled notes and at least one year taken off the life of my car, and five from mine, I returned home mentally, emotionally and physically exhausted.

The journey had not been without problems, nearly all of which were due to the weather, for without doubt I suffered everything that an intemperate British winter is capable of throwing at the unfortunate motorist. I could hardly foresee that I would be washing glasses and serving drinks behind the bar of a village pub, where I became snowbound for two days and nights.

Never, in my wildest imagination, could I have prepared for the eventuality of sharing the A1 with over 300 lorry drivers all, like me, firmly stuck in the snow. Had I done so, I would have included in my luggage a receptacle appropriate to deal with the natural and relentless bodily functions of this life. I now have extreme envy of the male species and a profound admiration for Eskimo women. The police patrolman, who wiped the snow from the windscreen of my car, grinned broadly as he read the label exhorting people to 'leave me room to drive away quickly'. "I've got news for you," he said. "You're not going anywhere, let alone quickly!"

Nothing in a nurse's training equips her to grapple with driving in a white-out, or on black ice, or in freezing fog. Neither is there a handy manual that advises you of the correct procedure to adopt when you fall asleep at the wheel of a car on the outside lane of the M1, at 70mph on a Friday evening. The mere fact that I survived these excursions says an awful lot for my guardian angel. Nevertheless, it was without doubt one of the most rewarding experiences possible and highlighted the many different problems with which people of all ages are faced on a regular basis.

Whilst the families of children dying from disease have some chance to prepare themselves for the final tragedy, what about those youngsters whose lives are terminated abruptly by the unforeseen, without any warning? The road traffic accident or the unpredictable disaster is a far more common event and strikes with a cruel suddenness.

Fifteen-year-old David went out to play with three school friends during the holidays – a normal occurrence in homes up and down the country. The only difference being that David never came home, for he was electrocuted when a piece of metal piping he was holding touched an overhead power cable. He died instantly, whilst his companions were all injured. Two years after the event, I spoke with the parents who were still struggling to come to terms with the trauma.

One of the immediate factors which they found both intrusive and distressing was the huge media attention. The film crews and reporters outside their house may have been pandering to the sensationalist appetites of the public at large, but gave little or no consideration to the feelings and privacy of those struggling to cope with the immediate shock and grief.

"We felt as if we were under siege and any family members, whose comfort we would have welcomed, had to run the gauntlet of their feeding frenzy."

Another problem was the necessity for funeral arrangements to be made quickly, before they had time to think things through. Under pressure from grandparents they opted for burial whereas, in retrospect, they would have preferred cremation. David's mother now felt drawn constantly to visit the grave whilst having to contend with the perpetual question from her little daughter: 'If David has gone to heaven to be with Jesus, why is he in the ground?'

The effect on the two other siblings, a boy of 14 and a girl of 17, had been disastrous. David was the leader and his mother likened the three children to a log with David as the centre – "both ends fell apart when he was removed." The sister became withdrawn and reluctant to go out with friends and spent a lot of time compiling verses on death and writing inscriptions for tombstones. The brother slipped further and further back in his school work and required the attention of a psychiatrist.

Mondays, the day of David's death, remained bad days and at three o'clock, the time he was due back on that fateful day, his mother still found herself listening for the door to open. "I just don't feel as if he isn't coming home, even after all this time."

The family weren't 'religious' as they put it but welcomed the ministrations of their vicar and found him pleasant, helpful and easy to talk to.

"It's difficult to explain, but our need is more for 'feeling help' than 'practical help'," they said. "We can cope with the daily tasks but the person we really value is the one who only comes to sit quietly, and is prepared to listen without constantly trying to make conversation."

The trouble is that in today's world of fast communication networks we haven't been taught a language where nothing is actually said. But what merit there can be sometimes in companionable silence. For these reasons, charities such as The Samaritans or Cruse prove invaluable.

Of all the experiences and encounters during my tour, one stood out to highlight the problems of grief and bereavement more than any other. On a snowy day in a small town in Wales, I was privileged to meet a mother who had lost her child in the Aberfan disaster of 1966, a unique tragedy which, hopefully, will never happen again. Although to the world at large it was an event soon pushed well to the back of our memories, to those involved it remained a terrible reality and, for some, the effects were still being felt many years later. This courageous woman quietly worked through her emotions and feelings from that fateful day until the present time, and the telling of them can provide a useful guide for everyone whether professional or lay person. The experience of Mrs. X can also be the problems of anyone suffering the loss of a loved one:

"The initial reaction was that of shock, numbness and a total disbelief which temporarily seemed to act as an anaesthetic. I moved about almost in a state of unawareness – all was confusion and the reality of the situation took time to dawn. Anger and bitterness were present in all of us for a long time and it took different forms: anger directed towards those we blamed for the accident; anger towards God for allowing it to happen; anger at the press and television who pestered and misreported and generally helped to make the situation worse.

"Then there was the bitterness and envy we felt towards those who hadn't lost a child and were, therefore, immune from grief in our eyes. Some of us felt very anti one or more of our surviving children and we became angry and confused because we couldn't understand why. Then the anger would be replaced temporarily by guilt because we felt we hadn't done enough to prevent the occurrence of such a tragedy, and the guilt led to aggression against those we held responsible. As these emotions subsided, so some became withdrawn into a bereavement group where we could grieve together without boring anyone. All I wanted to do was to talk about it over and over and over again.

"Our surviving children suffered either from over-protection, or even neglect if we became totally immersed in our sorrow. My own seven-year-old daughter became a surrogate mother to me overnight and undertook certain responsibilities because I wasn't functioning properly.

"Well-meaning doctors pumped me full of sedatives and tranquilisers which only served to hinder and prolong the whole process. It took five years before I could dispense with them, and my triumph came on the day that I was able to flush them down the toilet.

"Certain people aggravated us, especially the well-meaning 'do-gooders' who, in fact, had quite the reverse effect. I cringe at the trite remarks offered which only served to irritate. The person who placed a hand on my arm and said: 'I know just how you feel,' – but they didn't, they couldn't. The woman who said: 'At least you have the comfort of knowing that your child is in a better place than this rotten world.' That was no comfort whatsoever, I simply wanted my child. Yet another favourite was: 'You must be thankful that you still have your little girl.' I was thankful and I didn't need to be told so, but it didn't alter the fact that I had lost my little boy. 'Better to have loved and lost than never to have known him.' There was no ending to the pat phrases and platitudes which were poured upon us.

"The men suffered too, but in a different way. They were never really allowed to grieve, for they were considered to be 'tough valley men' and 'tough valley men' don't cry. My own husband spent five years patiently propping me up, and the day I finally came to terms with myself I saw him begin to visibly relax. Shortly afterwards, though, he himself experienced a physical breakdown in health which led to a coronary heart attack and diabetes."

One of the most serious mistakes we can make is to refuse to express our grief or to keep it bottled up. Medical authorities tell us that mismanagement of grief causes all sorts of physical and mental problems. There is a saying: 'When the eyes refuse to cry, other organs in the body will begin to weep instead, so let the tears flow.' Even 12 years later this man still hadn't done his grieving. He couldn't talk to anyone about his little boy, either leaving the room when his name was mentioned, or withdrawing completely. The daughter also became a victim of delayed reaction and suffered a mental breakdown shortly after entering college.

The country has largely forgotten and moved on and I don't think anyone fully understands quite how long deep grief can persist, nor its cumulative effects.

Nevertheless, there were some positive outcomes. Both women agreed that, having had to cope with such tragedies, they can now face anything. For them, nothing else that life threw at them could possibly be as bad. Similarly, they had a much better understanding of how to react toward others in like circumstances.

This poignant meeting returned to haunt me only nine years later when the ferry, *The Herald of Free Enterprise*, capsized off Zeebrugge. Three of my patients lost family members who were part of the crew. It was also a few hours before my husband and I learnt whether his son, who was employed on the ship, had been involved.

As a result of my tour, three glaring points emerged. Training of the caring professionals on the subject of dying, grief and bereavement had progressed little over the years. In my early nursing days it was virtually non-existent and I now found it still to be woefully inadequate. Students to whom I spoke were, more often than not, distressed, uncertain and critical of current teaching to meet their needs in this sphere. Most tutors were equally unhappy and some efforts were being made to amend the situation, but far more needed to be done.

There was also a yawning void in the education of the public at large, many of whom still regarded death as a taboo subject. Today, the situation is little better and, as a nation, we have developed an odd relationship with grief. It's not just that we are fascinated by tragedies; we are deeply moved and often surprised by our own reaction to them. National disasters hit the headlines and the country goes into collective mourning. Flowers, teddy bears and candles pile up at makeshift shrines, vigils are kept and people queue to sign books of condolence. However, the death of anyone, from whatever cause, is someone's Aberfan or Zeebrugge, and can easily go unacknowledged.

Feelings of deep sadness, loss, sleeplessness, crying, tiredness, depression and lack of appetite, are all part of the natural process of grieving. Grief, however, is not an illness; it is more helpful to think of it as part of being human, and a perfectly normal response to the death of a loved one. To treat it otherwise can be dangerously simplistic and fatally flawed. Well-intentioned family members, who cannot bear to see a relative in such deep emotional pain, will often approach a doctor or nurse with a plea that they be prescribed something to help them to 'get over it'. Death, however, isn't something which we conveniently 'get over', but learn to come to terms with instead. It can't conveniently be resolved by taking a pill and it takes time and patience before we can eventually begin to move on.

Medicalisation of the bereaved is really not helpful. Tranquilisers and anti-depressants may sedate or dull the senses for a while but they bring with them the risk of dependency. At some stage there will come a point when the sufferer has to wake up and face reality.

For those who are grieving, it is much better to offer time as a way to help; time to listen, time for compassion, time to empathise, time to assess whether, in fact, there are practical suggestions for providing support. Time, however, appears to be a precious commodity in the modern world where everyone professes to be busy, busy, busy.

As a result of this experience, bereavement visiting became very much part of the district nursing role. There was never an excuse to feel that, if things were slack, there wasn't anything to do. Consequently, team members tried to find a moment when they would call in on the most vulnerable patients who had experienced loss whilst in our care. Frequently this meant visiting the lonely widow or widower, especially the very aged and those without family support, and those where the death had been particularly sudden or tragic. The small, tell-tale signs of self-neglect would occasionally alert us to the fact that all was not well.

Bereavement is all about 'letting go' and moving on and something we tend only to associate with the death of someone we love. Yet, if we think about it our lives are made up of 'letting go' experiences. At birth we are parted abruptly from the security of the womb. The day comes when we have to leave the safety of our mother's side and start school, and so it is throughout life.

There are other factors which can promote feelings of bereavement – divorce, redundancy, loss of health, amputation of a part of the body, all may engender feelings of grief and longing for things as they once were. Learning to 'let go' is something we all have to face at some time.

Julian was a remarkable person and had everything to live for. Tall, good-looking, possessed with a fine business brain, highly regarded and respected by his peers, superior achievements in his career, a beautiful home, an attractive wife and two teenage children doing well at public school. Then cancer struck but, shock as it was to this man, it was merely a blip on the screen of life.

I knew Julian as one of the church family in the village and from having attended the family in my capacity as a midwife. Without doubt he became an example and inspiration to everyone. Sunday by Sunday he joined us with his chemotherapy pump strapped to him as he faced the adversary determinedly and with humour.

The wonderful day came when he received the 'all clear' from the hospital, but with it came the most unexpected and devastating personal blow, when his wife left him for someone else. I held my breath, fearful as to how this would affect him. After the first heart-breaking shock, he faced this added unwanted burden with dignity and resolve.

Still Julian's problems weren't over. The cancer returned, but three times he went into remission, raising his hopes and those of us all. In the autumn, however, the dread disease struck its hardest blow and it slowly became clear that, despite everything, the battle was being lost. A week before Christmas Julian sat in his pew, his body bearing cruel testimony to its attacker, and he said to me: "Ann, I think the time has come for me to let go. I'll get Christmas over, and the children and I will enjoy that, but I think that will be the end."

So it was that, in mid-January, a packed church paid tribute to an amazing man in a service which he himself had prepared. His death wasn't a failure but total victory, for Julian had played it his way and had been prepared to let go when the time came.

Julian made the decision to let go for himself, but what about the husband, wife, parent or child who refuses to let go of their nearest and dearest? During my time as a District Nurse I well recall a delightful gentleman in his early eighties. His wife was a semi-invalid and they had no children, simply living for one another. He positively adored her, spoiled her and did everything for her, a tragedy in itself as she was later to prove more than capable of doing the many tasks he undertook in the belief that he was protecting her.

Then illness struck and the multiple operations he underwent proved unsuccessful, merely mutilating his body which became a mass of tubes, bags and unhealed wounds. After endless weeks of watching this valiant but exhausted man struggle to maintain life for the sake of the clinging little woman who hardly left his side, the inevitable day came when she faced me in tears and said: "Sister, I can't bear to see him like this any longer."

Very gently the colleague who was with me tried to explain that the solution was in her hands. "Your husband is only hanging onto life for your sake," she said. "In fact, he needs your permission and assurance to allow him to let go."

Quietly and movingly she held his hand telling him of her love, reassuring him of her ability to cope on her own and her desire that he should find peace and release from his suffering. In less than 24 hours he quietly died.

These presented two very different examples of 'letting go'.

How we regard death and how we respond to it can have a considerable effect on the bereavement period that follows. Mercifully, for the vast majority bereavement is a natural process and one which people work through unaided. Nevertheless, for those who refuse to accept death as part of the cycle of life and rail against it, difficulties can and do arise.

However, it is essential to retain a sense of proportion as only a relatively small percentage of the population will require the help of professionals in this matter. For every person who presents as a bereavement problem, many more will cope quite normally with the process unaided. If we begin to look at every mourner as a potential problem, he or she will undoubtedly become one.

Chapter Ten.
Things Ain't What They Used To Be

 The National Health Service was created in 1948, to serve a society wearied by war and accustomed to austerity. However, there remained considerable resilience, humour and a sense of fun within the community. People who were used to little were content with simple things. Cinema, sport and radio, combined with 'holidays at home' or the British seaside and Butlin's camps were virtually all that was on offer. Television and travel abroad were both in their infancy and beyond the reach of most. In a popular song Max Bygraves later bemoaned the loss of the local Palais for nights out dancing, trams which had been replaced by traffic jams, and a paddle at Southend now overtaken by foreign holidays. Times they were a'changing.

However, at no point in our history has change occurred at such a rate as has been witnessed in the last 40 years, especially socially and within nursing and the NHS. Such a health scheme which was available free for everyone, was a noble concept but none could have foreseen the huge advances which would take place within an exceedingly short timeframe. It is anyone's guess whether Britain, with the benefit of hindsight, would still have chosen to follow the same route to universal health care.

In 1967 the first human heart transplant was carried out and two years later man landed on the moon. Achievements like these dictated that change was inevitable and occurring at a pace that was difficult to keep up with. Advances in science and technology began to have a massive impact and the Health Service has been beset by increasing problems. Faced on the one hand with ever-escalating costs as a result of progress in medical knowledge, medicines and machinery, and on the other with financial restrictions inevitable in a centrally funded operation, plus its changing management dogmas and political beliefs, the NHS has become a difficult vessel to steer.

From the earliest days of the NHS, its senior managers and successive governments have been challenged on many different fronts: its organisation and administration; finding adequate funding and balancing the often conflicting demands and unrealistic expectations of patients, staff and taxpayers. Bevan foresaw this when he spoke to nurses at a conference of the Royal College of Nursing. "We shall never have all we need," he said. "Expectations will always exceed capacity and it will grow, change, improve, yet always appear inadequate." Even he could not have foreseen the extent to which this would prove to be true.

Since the end of the '60s the NHS has been in an almost continuous state of reorganisation, or what some would call re-disorganisation. Sadly there is little evidence that structured changes produced much in the way of benefits, although most were seldom left in place long enough for anyone to be able to tell. Endless reports from Salmon, Cumberlege, Griffiths, Warnock and Calman have appeared, to name but a few, all spawning countless recommendations.

From my own point of view, the reorganisation of the NHS in 1974 had quite an impact. The aim was to bring together hospital and community services. All local health services were transferred from the control of County Councils to the newly formed Regional and Area Health Authorities, which were then promptly abolished in 1982 in favour of District Health Authorities. Social Services were separated from Health which was much criticised and has proved far from satisfactory. This loss of integration between the health and social care systems has created many problems, provoking calls for the re-amalgamation of the two bodies.

Modern, purpose-built Health Centres began to appear, including two in the rural area in which I worked. Many of us thought heaven had come nearer to earth as superior supplies and stocks of medical equipment were regularly delivered and constantly to hand, including Central Sterile Supplies which made our lives so much easier. Gone was the need to make up dressings for our patients, although I did frequently fret about the amount of waste generated as superfluous contents of dressing packs were simply thrown away. We were beginning to reap the whirlwind of the wastefulness incurred by living in a disposable society.

Invaluable State Enrolled Nurses and Nursing Auxilliaries arrived on the district, adding greatly to the concept of Primary Health Care Teams. A room was provided for the district nurses where we each had a desk with large drawers in which to file records. The Health visitors were similarly equipped and situated in an adjacent room which made for better liaison.

Importantly, a desperately needed twilight nursing service was established in 1982. Operative between 7.00 and 11.00 p.m, it took some of the pressure off the district nurses and provided improved support for those patients being nursed at home, especially the terminally ill and dying. However, it took longer before a full night nursing service in the community was introduced. Sadly, within a short time, the decision had to be taken to send the nurses out in pairs in order to ensure their safety. This was neither labour nor cost-effective and it is a crying indictment of present day society that surgery, hospital and community staff and even the emergency services are now subject to unbelievable levels of abuse from the very public they are trying to help. Perhaps I should consider myself very lucky that, in all the years that I went out alone in the evenings and at night, I never once experienced anything that gave me cause to worry on this account.

Following the recommendations of the Salmon Report in 1967 attempts were made to raise the profile of the nursing profession within hospital management. As a result the hierarchical structure of nursing also changed and in came line managers, ward managers and clinical nurse managers, all of which were roles typically undertaken by senior nurses. This was often seen as a natural career progression with better financial rewards. Many nurses who had worked in practical settings for a long time chose to leave clinical nursing and join the ranks of NHS management. This marked the start of an obsession with titles. People became desperate to underline their perceived importance, or ensure their correct status with the appropriate handle: Executives, Officers, Controllers, Commissioners, Consultants, Directors, Administrators, Supervisors, Specialists and Managers. All appeared in order to confuse, impress and clearly stamp their position on the professional ladder.

However, there was no such career pathway apparent for those nurses who wished to remain at the bedside in order to retain close patient contact and care. 'Too many chiefs but not enough Indians' became the cry as tiers of management and government, who had seldom rolled up their sleeves, or had long forgotten what it was like at the coal face or the grass roots out in the field, dictated the policies.

'Too posh to wash' became a popular expression as elitist,

specialist nurses came into being, hot on advice giving but short on the delivery of practical care. Even if allowances are made for exaggeration and the comments are taken with a pinch of salt, there is often more than a grain of truth attached.

As the 1980s progressed and technology advanced, the spectre of the computer began to rear its head. District nurses suddenly found themselves equipped with hand-held Kalamazoos on which to record every detail of each visit made, the time taken and the distance covered. It was by no means universally welcomed and its life was of short duration as the omnipresent computer began to appear in every department, including GP surgeries. Now taken for granted, for many of us this required the mastery of a completely different skill, not to mention the time it took to input the data.

The cost incurred by all these improvements or innovations was considerable. Coupled with new and sophisticated surgical requirements, such as organ transplants, and the demands being made by every specialty for an increased share of the financial cake, the expenditure was forever escalating.

A burgeoning pharmaceutical industry had created a flood of expensive new drugs and continues to do so. Antibiotics, 'flu vaccines, better anaesthetic agents, the contraceptive pill, steroids, drugs for the treatment of mental illness such as schizophrenia, depression and Alzheimer's, good diuretics for heart failure and chemotherapy medication — the list is endless. The insidious, creeping medicalisation of everyday life has also increased reliance on drugs to address lifestyle factors, such as raised cholesterol levels, without patients taking any responsibility to effect the necessary changes for themselves.

Procedures such as gastric band operations to combat obesity, breast enhancement or reduction, and gender reassignment measures, jockey for position in the operating theatres alongside life-threatening conditions. Despite the availability of free contraception, abortion rates have risen. A steady increase in alcohol abuse has caused turmoil for ambulance crews and the staff in A&E departments. Both simply add to the financial expenditure. Is it not time that these patients should be billed for their treatment? Why bother to modify, or give up the things we like, or put up with the things we don't, if we can simply take a tablet or have an operation, at no cost and little inconvenience to ourselves?

Quite apart from any financial implications, some medications cause as many problems as they solve. This creates a vicious cycle and has a significant part to play in the rising drug bill as yet another prescription is given to correct the side effects.

The sting lies in the enormous expenditure involved. It was so soul-destroying, on clearing a patient's house following a death, to discover the hoards of prescribed medicines which had accumulated over time. All of these had to be safely destroyed and I can recall an exercise I did in 1980 to attempt to quantify this. From one very average home I removed pills and potions to the total of £106.40. Magnify this across the country and it isn't difficult to see just one effect of progress in terms of cost.

Nevertheless, drug taking in the '80s was as nothing compared to the present. Britain has fast become a nation of 'pill-poppers'. This has led to many problems, not least the projected antibiotic crisis with which we are threatened. The antibiotics used to treat even minor wound infections, as well as far more serious conditions, are rapidly losing their effectiveness in the face of ever more resistant germs. With a lack of new ones to take their place, we are now faced with a situation which could herald the end of modern medicine as we know it.

As early as 1976, many of us predicted that the casual way in which some doctors prescribed antibiotics would result in this very situation if they continued to be used so frequently and inappropriately. However, the public at large must also take a share of the responsibility.

In the early days people regarded Health Care as a privilege, not an automatic right. They trusted the doctors to do their best for them and certainly wouldn't dream of telling them what to prescribe. By the 1980s antibiotics were frequently being given out, often under patient pressure, to tackle colds and other viral infections for which they do no good. People with no medical knowledge were not happy unless they left the surgery clutching the prescription which they felt was needed and theirs by right. Now we are paying the price.

Other agencies are also to blame. Bacteria which cause disease have become immune, not only to drugs but also to the multiplicity of antibacterial sprays which are advertised and marketed so aggressively. These obliterate both good and bad bacteria without discrimination. This in turn destroys the body's natural immunity. In our efforts to promote improved standards of hygiene, washing with good old soap and water has been superseded by a multiplicity of agents which have been introduced in an attempt to control a spate of major infections, such as MRSA and C. Difficile.

However, other enemies lie lurking in the woodpile to tax a seemingly beleaguered Health Service. The country is now faced with managing yet another threat to the nation's well-being. Whereas cancer was deemed to be the scourge of the 20th century, Alzheimer's is set to replace it in the 21st. It is likely to be among the most costly of diseases for society in Europe and the USA, and will increase with an ever-ageing society. 1:85 people are predicted to be effected by 2050.

In 1970 when I embarked upon District Nursing, dementia was nowhere near as prevalent as it is today and Alzheimer's disease was not a word known to most of us. People were referred to as 'the confused elderly', 'senile' or, less charitably, 'out of their tree' or, 'they've lost their marbles'. Many were able to be cared for at home with good family support, whilst others were admitted to the psycho-geriatric units attached to hospitals, or into the care of Social Services.

From the end of the '80s Alzheimer's disease has emerged from obscurity. Once considered a rare disorder it is now a major health problem. It is one of the most common causes of loss of mental function known broadly as dementia. It was first described in 1906 but has undoubtedly existed throughout history, albeit not on this scale.

The symptoms progress from loss of present recall, to confusion, irritability, aggression and mood swings, to trouble with speech and language, long-term memory failure and loss of bodily functions. Gradually the sufferer withdraws from society. The strain imposed upon the family by this disease is tremendous.

As more and more are admitted to the ever increasing number of private nursing homes and residential care units currently being built, the associated costs of such long-term institutionalisation by Health Care professionals, or that occasioned by day care at home, will be enormous. This in turn is having an effect on staffing levels.

Another huge impact has resulted from the changes made in nurse education. In the 1990s out went the first level nurse, or SRN, and second level training for State Enrolled Nurses was no longer provided. The latter has been one of the greatest losses to the profession.

In their place the modern era has seen the development of nursing degrees. Nurse training, even if not divorced from the bedside, is sufficiently far removed and considerably more academically based. The drive to turn nursing into a profession, underpinned by a degree, has made it harder for the less academic to enter a field where A' levels in the sciences aren't much use when you're helping the incontinent and confused elderly.

Some graduates eventually tend to work within key roles in the NHS or choose to specialise and undertake much of the work previously performed by doctors. The new role of Nurse Practitioner has been created, requiring a minimum of a Bachelor's Degree in nursing. They perform roles similar to those of physicians and can prescribe medications, commonly working in GP surgeries or A&E departments. There are now specialist community public health nurses and Practice Nurses who are fulfilling a part of the once traditional District Nurse and Health Visitor roles, but the old multi-tasking, good, all-round, generalist nurse is rapidly becoming a creature of the past.

Nurses now spend every available minute churning out notes, or attached to the computer providing reams of documentation, largely to cover their backs, most of which will never be read. The result is that more and more is being written about the patients and less and less time actually spent alongside them. Reports appear in the media of people being left unfed, unwashed and un-toileted, to the extent that if a person is seen to be breathing they are deemed to be self-caring. This is not an exaggeration but something I had cause to experience to my cost.

Financial constraints alone are not solely responsible for the current flaws. Badly trained staff who are often poorly deployed appear to receive little or no supervision. They are allowed to be selective in the hours they are prepared to work at a stretch in order to obtain longer periods off duty. Not only does this call into question their safety to practice, but tiredness will inevitably make them more irritable and lacking in patience. The patient then becomes just a 'task' to be dealt with and 'ticked off' in the appropriate box, rather than an individual.

Pride in the profession is disappearing along with the traditional uniforms and a relaxing of discipline, to the point where the staff now appear more interested in meeting targets, ticking boxes and writing notes than they are in the needs of the patients. Once upon a time applicants for training would start by saying how much they wanted to look after people. Now their only interest is how they see their career advancing, preferably within the shortest possible time.

In the scramble to provide sufficient personnel to staff, not only our hospitals but the steadily increasing numbers of nursing and residential homes, much use is being made of Care Assistants. They play a key role in supporting qualified professionals in a health care environment. Although they may not need any specific qualifications it is often possible to work towards a National Vocational Qualification in health and social care. Those who have passed Level Three can begin formal nurse training if they so desire. Whilst in no way wishing to denigrate this role, they too often form the bulk of staff in many care homes. The standards appear to vary considerably and have been the subject of much scrutiny and criticism at times. It is only necessary to scan any Situations Vacant column in local newspapers to discover the pressing need for this level of employee. The concern is that, with the present chronic shortage of jobs available, people will be drawn to apply simply because they need the money not because they really want to undertake such work. Caring is a vocation and empathy a gift.

By the early '70s, the role of matron was abolished as part of the reorganisation recommended by the Salmon Report. Matron was once the most senior nurse in hospital and responsible for all nurses and domestic staff, overseeing patient care, staffing and the general efficiency of the hospital. It was a role memorably associated with the formidable film character played by Hattie Jacques, or TV's slightly less intimidating Wendy Craig in *The Royal*.

Forty years later, in response to various press complaints of dirty, ineffective hospitals with poorly disciplined staff, high infection rates and falling standards of basic patient care, a cry went up to 'Bring back the Matron'. She, or he, is now reappearing. However, it is no use simply reinstating a title without according the influence and authority that once went with it. At one time there was no mistaking precisely who and what the matron was. Nowadays they are indistinguishable from the stream of ordinarily dressed people filling the hospital wards and corridors. Their powers are limited and they spend most of the time on administrative work rather than having direct responsibility in the sphere of patient care.

"I am nothing more than a glorified bed-manager for the hospital," one remarked to me.

Some areas employ Community Matrons whose role is

predominantly clinical. They have a caseload of patients for whom they are responsible, many of whom have chronic health conditions which generally result in multiple hospital admissions. It is the aim of this staff group to treat the patient within the community, wherever possible, thereby limiting bed occupancy. This was once part of the role of the district nurse.

All these efforts are very laudable and necessary, but with a chronic shortage of adequately trained staff there is a limit to what can be achieved.

The situation for medical staff has also been affected by the reduction of working hours for doctors. With the implementation of a new out-of-hours visiting system patients no longer enjoy the services of a doctor from their own practice night and day. House calls by a GP are becoming an increasing rarity. Both they and district nurses now seem to think that a phone call to check on the wellbeing of a patient is sometimes all that is required. Verbal questioning from a distance is no substitute for actual observation which, all too often, can reveal an altogether different picture.

Today the nurse must be professional, and may also be a technical expert, administrator or executive. Nevertheless, what people want above all else is kindness and respect, compassion, limitless patience and a sense of humour. These are essential ingredients in any form of care, especially in the case of the elderly and confused, and the long-term chronocially sick. However, kindness and compassion are inherent qualities that cannot be taught. "Professionalising" care won't produce compassion – the best carers have the right attitude as well as qualifications. Furthermore, they need to be freed from paperwork and allowed to get on with the real job of looking after people.

No one wants a return to the 'old days' but somewhere along the road nursing has lost its way. 'Put the friendly faces back on the wards,' and 'Teach the nurses how to smile,' the newspaper headlines blare. 'Let us ensure that patients are treated with dignity, compassion and respect,' says another. The mere fact that a Prime Minister has to announce a £1 million scheme to identify best nursing practice, and introduce new standards that will restore a sense of pride in the profession, is indicative of a huge problem. We need to constantly remind ourselves exactly what nursing is about and who a nurse really is.

Nurses care for individuals of all ages and backgrounds in a holistic manner based on their physical, emotional, psychological, social and spiritual needs. Nursing involves the use of clinical judgment in the administration of this care in order to enable people to improve, maintain, or recover health.

Perhaps one of the greatest differences I have noticed, over a nursing career spanning some 40 years, is in the attitude of the public. In the 1970s the expectations of my patients were modest. They were far more appreciative and grateful, far less demanding with few complaints being made. Now, people complain about anything and everything. The advent of litigation and a compensation culture is costing billions, and this has had a disastrous effect on staff morale, whilst also imposing a huge financial drain on an already cash-strapped service.

In the present 'Me, Me, Me Society' there is a persistent clamour by some to attain their desires. "I want it, I must have it and I must have it now," seems to be the mantra. We live in a world of instant gratification in which everything we crave is considered ours by right, preferably at little or no cost.

Gone too are the principles of self-reliance. We have now become accustomed to the comfortable cushion of a 'nanny state' that absolves us from thinking or taking any responsibility for ourselves. People have become so dependent on that almighty fairy godmother to sort out their problems from the cradle to the grave, with the result that expectations are now totally unrealistic.

When Sir William Beveridge wrote his report in 1942 arguing for the creation of the welfare state, he simply wanted to give the poor a hand up from the grim life they faced. Unintentionally, such a move created a climate of welfare dependency and a sense of entitlement.

In the 1970s when trying to persuade deserving and needy patients to apply for benefits there was still a measure of reluctance. This was especially true among the elderly who regarded it as the stigma associated with charity and it went against their pride to accept. However, such nicety of feeling didn't last long. Within a short time frame there has emerged an awareness that not only is it possible to get something for nothing but that we have a right to. It has created a culture of benefit dependency and an age of entitlement which has also impacted the Health Service.

There are many who feel it shameful that care of the elderly is now seen as the practical and financial responsibility of the state. However, this is as much due to social and demographic changes as to filial reluctance. Most women are now working and have to juggle home life with care of children and grandchildren, leaving neither the time nor physical stamina to devote to senior family members. Sheer distance is a major consideration as older children are now likely to be scattered nationwide, if not worldwide, in pursuit of job opportunities. In the face of ever-increasing longevity this is posing a considerable problem, not only for government and the caring agencies, but also for families and the worried elderly themselves.

In 2008 the End Life Care Strategy document was produced. This aimed to promote dignity in dying and to provide people approaching the end of life with more choice about where and how they would like to live or die. It also proposed allowing them to exercise choice with regard to their care and treatment. Support of family and carers during the patient's life and after bereavement is also strongly advocated and, as in the past, charitable bodies, such as Marie Curie and the Hospice Movement, are already spearheading the way.

There is no doubt that we are now living in a very different culture, and one to which everyone is either trying to adapt, redefine or modify, in the face of escalating financial problems. I look back on those days on the district with considerable fondness, profoundly grateful that I was able to work at the time I did, in such a varied environment, free to use the skills I had learned and simply to get on with the job without being hampered by many of today's constraints.

Ann, with her parents outside the surgery, after receiving the Canterbury and Thanet Long Service Award

Without doubt they were among the happiest and most fulfilling of my life.

I certainly wouldn't wish to see a return to many of the fairly primitive social conditions which prevailed, nor some of the archaic health practices. I can and do rejoice, marvel at and give thanks for much of the progress, discovery and innovation that have been made.

Yet I also find much to question and criticise and still mourn the loss of many things that were good in an era that has largely passed away into the history books.

Epilogue

On that day in 1972 when I diffidently set off on the path to District Nursing I could not possibly have foreseen where it would take me. I certainly never thought that I'd remain in the post for 18 years nor experience all that I did. Neither did I imagine the role would prove to be so fulfilling, both professionally and personally.

Founding a Hospice couldn't have been further from my thoughts and the possibility of being honoured for doing so never even featured on the horizon.

Above left: Ann receives the Order of the British Empire at Buckingham Palace

Above right: Ann receives a Special Recognition Award from Alan Milburn, Minister of Health, at the 2001 Nurse of the Year Awards

However, there is always something very satisfying about receiving professional acclaim from one's peers.

This book is a tribute to the many people without whom none of this would have happened: the patients who motivated me; the doctors and staff of a wonderful GP practice who nurtured me; the camaraderie of my nursing colleagues across the area who worked alongside me and the amazing love, support and encouragement of my wonderful, long-suffering family.